Essential Maths

Book 7C

Answers

Elmwood Press

First published 2008 by
Elmwood Press
80 Attimore Road
Welwyn Garden City
Herts. AL8 6LP
Tel. 01707 333232

ISBN 9781 902 214 832

Typeset and illustrated by Domex e-Data Pvt. Ltd.
Printed in Great Britain by Face Communications Ltd.
www.facecommunications.co.uk

Unit 1

Page 1 **Exercise 1M**

1. (a) 3000   (b) 90   (c) 70000   **2.** (a) 85 707   (b) 86 607

  (c) 85 617   (d) 95 607   (e) 85 608   (f) 185 607   **3.** (a) 500

  (b) 30   (c) 60 000   (d) 800   (e) 7000   (f) 300 000

  (g) 50 000   (h) 6 000 000   **4.** (a) 5835   (b) 49 500   (c) 2203

  (d) 545 000   **5.** 300   **6.** 20   **7.** 30   **8.** 600

9. 7000   **10.** 40   **11.** 60 000, 10   **12.** (a) 299   (b) 6699

  (c) 4490   (d) 490   (e) 6900   (f) 6499

13. A 340,   B 490,   C 620,   D 5100,   E 6600,   F 7900

14. (a) 409   (b) 6401   (c) 16211   (d) 500 000   (e) 400 050

  (f) 3500   **15.** (a) 8643   (b) 3468   **16.** (a) 96 540   (b) 40 569

17. (a) six hundred and seventy-five thousand   (b) many possibilities

Page 3 **Exercise 1E**

1. (a)

+	100	10	1	1000
1437	1537	1447	1438	2437
499	599	509	500	1499
2917	3017	2927	2918	3917
6043	6143	6053	6044	7043

(b)

+	20	300	5	100
380	400	680	385	480
796	816	1096	801	896
905	925	1205	910	1005
32	52	332	37	132

2. (a) 580   (b) 679   (c) 1579   **3.** (a) 2703   (b) 2383   (c) 1683

4. Twenty-two thousand one hundred and sixty-five

5. $1000 + 547 - 100$ **6.** (a) six thousand two hundred   (b) ninety thousand

  (c) twenty-five thousand and ten   (d) six hundred and ten thousand four hundred

  (e) seven million ten thousand

7. (a) 98 643   (b) 43 698   **8.** (a) 361   (b) 409   (c) 7035

9. (a) 1425   (b) 7423   (c) 25 100   **10.** (a) 0 before decimal point

  (b) 46 000   **11.** (a) 2058, 2136, 2142, 2290   (b) 5029, 5299, 5329, 5330

  (c) 25000, 25 117, 25 171, 25 200, 25 500   **12.** $n = 100$ **13.** $p = 10$

14. $a = 100, b = 7$ **15.** $p = 1000, q = 10$

Page 5   ***Exercise 2M***

1. 163	**2.** 221	**3.** 219	**4.** 296	**5.** 633
6. 782	**7.** 657	**8.** 990	**9.** 1022	**10.** 1530
11. 1206	**12.** 1400	**13.** 124	**14.** 287	**15.** 1201
16. 396	**17.** 173	**18.** 5103	**19.** 317	**20.** 746
21. 3265	**22.** 2104	**23.** 6813	**24.** 2920	**25.** 2008
26. 6242	**27.** 8845	**28.** 3662	**29.** 58 329	**30.** 27 263
31. 65 656	**32.** 163 551			

Page 6   ***Exercise 2E***

^{1}5	^{2}7		^{3}9	7	^{4}6		^{5}9	1
^{6}8	0	9			^{7}4	1	1	
2			^{8}5	6	4		^{9}4	3
			8			^{10}9		
^{11}9		^{12}7	5	^{13}9		^{14}4	1	^{15}7
3		6		^{16}7	1	7		2
^{17}3	1	9			8		^{18}8	9

Page 7   ***Exercise 3M***

1. 36	**2.** 77	**3.** 18	**4.** 35	**5.** 23
6. 405	**7.** 281	**8.** 208	**9.** 586	**10.** 390
11. 17	**12.** 17	**13.** 38	**14.** 27	**15.** 29
16. 85	**17.** 226	**18.** 458	**19.** 88	**20.** 1585

21. $784 - 627 = 157$ **22.** $635 - 429 = 206$ **23.** $6874 - 592 = 6282$

Page 8   ***Exercise 3E***

1. 214	**2.** 345	**3.** 755	**4.** 1293	**5.** 963
6. 360	**7.** 1155	**8.** 34	**9.** 385	**10.** 1075
11. 1900	**12.** 208	**13.** 106	**14.** 415	**15.** 1132
16. 119	**17.** 1075	**18.** 832	**19.** 261	**20.** 818
21. 5659	**22.** 6780	**23.** 1616		

24.

+	18	67	53	32
33	51	100	86	65
61	79	128	114	93
17	35	84	70	49
14	32	81	67	46

25. $234 - 65 = 169$

Page 9 Magic Squares

1.

4	3	8
9	5	1
2	7	6

2.

8	7	3
1	6	11
9	5	4

3.

3	10	8
12	7	2
6	4	11

4.

9	4	11
10	8	6
5	12	7

5.

6	7	2
1	5	9
8	3	4

6.

6	7	11
13	8	3
5	9	10

7.

3	6	10	15
16	9	5	4
13	12	8	1
2	7	11	14

8.

9	14	2	13
11	4	16	7
12	3	15	8
6	17	5	10

9.

11	8	5	10
2	13	16	3
14	1	4	15
7	12	9	6

Page 9 Exercise 4A Part A

1. 14	**2.** 10	**3.** 16	**4.** 18	**5.** 12	**6.** 24	**7.** 15
8. 18	**9.** 27	**10.** 21	**11.** 16	**12.** 28	**13.** 20	**14.** 32
15. 24	**16.** 15	**17.** 35	**18.** 40	**19.** 25	**20.** 45	**21.** 24
22. 42	**23.** 48	**24.** 36	**25.** 54	**26.** 21	**27.** 35	**28.** 42
29. 28	**30.** 49	**31.** 24	**32.** 56	**33.** 64	**34.** 72	**35.** 48
36. 9	**37.** 0	**38.** 63	**39.** 54	**40.** 81		

Part B

Grid 1

×	7	2	12	8	6	3	11	9	4	5
7	49	14	84	56	42	21	77	63	28	35
2	14	4	24	16	12	6	22	18	8	10
12	84	24	144	96	72	36	132	108	48	60
8	56	16	96	64	48	24	88	72	32	40
6	42	12	72	48	36	18	66	54	24	30
3	21	6	36	24	18	9	33	27	12	15
11	77	22	132	88	66	33	121	99	44	55
9	63	18	108	72	54	27	99	81	36	45
4	28	8	48	32	24	12	44	36	16	20
5	35	10	60	40	30	15	55	45	20	25

Grid 2

×	2	9	6	3	5	11	12	8	7	4
2	4	18	12	6	10	22	24	16	14	8
9	18	81	54	27	45	99	108	72	63	36
6	12	54	36	18	30	66	72	48	42	24
3	6	27	18	9	15	33	36	24	21	12
5	10	45	30	15	25	55	60	40	35	20
11	22	99	66	33	55	121	132	88	77	44
12	24	108	72	36	60	132	144	96	84	48
8	16	72	48	24	40	88	96	64	56	32
7	14	56	42	21	35	77	84	56	49	28
4	8	36	24	12	20	44	48	32	28	16

Page 10   **Exercise 4E**

1. (a)

×	9	8	2	7
5	45	40	10	35
4	36	32	8	28
3	27	24	6	21
6	54	48	12	42

(b)

×	4	7	3	8
5	20	35	15	40
9	36	63	27	72
6	24	42	18	48
2	8	14	6	16

(c)

×	4	5	8	2
3	12	15	24	6
7	28	35	56	14
6	24	30	48	12
9	36	45	72	18

(d)

×	4	5	3	8
2	8	10	6	16
9	36	45	27	72
6	24	30	18	48
7	28	35	21	56

(e)

×	3	7	4	9
8	24	56	32	72
2	6	14	8	18
5	15	35	20	45
6	18	42	24	54

(f)

×	2	5	7	4
9	18	45	63	36
8	16	40	56	32
3	6	15	21	12
6	12	30	42	24

(g)

×	2	7	8	3
5	10	35	40	15
4	8	28	32	12
6	12	42	48	18
9	18	63	72	27

(h)

×	2	8	6	9
3	6	24	18	27
7	14	56	42	63
5	10	40	30	45
4	8	32	24	36

(i)

×	5	6	3	8
7	35	42	21	56
2	10	12	6	16
4	20	24	12	32
9	45	54	27	72

(j)

×	9	7	4	8
2	18	14	8	16
5	45	35	20	40
6	54	42	24	48
3	27	21	12	24

(k)

×	7	4	5	8
2	14	8	10	16
6	42	24	30	48
9	63	36	45	72
3	21	12	15	24

(l)

×	3	2	5	7
4	12	8	20	28
8	24	16	40	56
9	27	18	45	63
6	18	12	30	42

or

×	3	9	5	7
4	12	36	20	28
8	24	72	40	56
2	6	18	10	14
6	18	54	30	42

2. (a)

×	6	2	7	4	5
8	48	16	56	32	40
3	18	6	21	12	15
9	54	18	63	36	45
7	42	14	49	28	35
5	30	10	35	20	25

(b)

×	4	9	7	3	8
6	24	54	42	18	48
7	28	63	49	21	56
3	12	27	21	9	24
5	20	45	35	15	40
4	16	36	28	12	32

(c)

×	3	6	4	8	9
7	21	42	28	56	63
8	24	48	32	64	72
5	15	30	20	40	45
9	27	54	36	72	81
3	9	18	12	24	27

Page 12 **Exercise 5M**

1. 170	**2.** 252	**3.** 225	**4.** 147	**5.** 408	**6.** 576
7. 595	**8.** 438	**9.** 92	**10.** 81	**11.** 112	**12.** 4
13. 76	**14.** 180	**15.** 1026	**16.** 2790	**17.** 3703	**18.** 5152
19. 5463	**20.** 2220	**21.** 29 512	**22.** 28 912	**23.** 8064	**24.** 6125

Page 12 **Exercise 5E**

1. 720 min **2.** £12 900 **3.** 120 **4.** 176 **5.** 238p

6. 4389 **7.** 468 **8.** 81m² **9.** (a) $47 \times 5 = 235$ (b) $326 \times 7 = 2282$

(c) $703 \times 8 = 5624$ **10.** (a) T (b) T **11.** $6851 + 31 = 6882$ **12.** $36\,057 + 101 = 36\,158$

Page 13 **Exercise 1M**

1. (a) 5 (b) 4 (c) 2 (d) 8 (e) 9 (f) 8
(g) 10 (h) 4 (i) 5 (j) 9 (k) 11 (l) 6
(m) 5 (n) 11 (o) 16 (p) 1 (q) 0 (r) 7
(s) 9 (t) 9 **2.** (a) 11 (b) 48 (c) 6 (d) 9
(e) 2 (f) 10 (g) 81 (h) 49 (i) 56 (j) 8
(k) 72 (l) 2 (m) 42 (n) 40 (o) 8

3. (a) $3 \times 5 = 15, 5 \times 3 = 15, 15 \div 5 = 3$ (b) $15 \times 5 = 75, 75 \div 5 = 15, 75 \div 15 = 5$
(c) $8 \times 12 = 96, 96 \div 8 = 12, 96 \div 12 = 8$ (d) $6 \times 16 = 96, 16 \times 6 = 96, 96 \div 16 = 6$

4. 40 **5.** 64

Page 14 **Exercise 1E**

1. (a) T (b) F (c) F (d) T (e) F (f) F
2. (a) 8 (b) 8 (c) 4 (d) 28 (e) 42 (f) 8
3. 8 **4.** 7 **5.** $(3 + 17) \div 5 = 4$

6.

×	7	4	9	3	6
6	42	24	54	18	36
5	35	20	45	15	30
8	56	32	72	24	48
9	63	36	81	27	54
7	49	28	63	21	42

7.

×	5	3	6	8	7
8	40	24	48	64	56
7	35	21	42	56	49
2	10	6	12	16	14
4	20	12	24	32	28
9	45	27	54	72	63

8.

×	6	7	9	8	4
7	42	49	63	56	28
5	30	35	45	40	20
9	54	63	81	72	36
3	18	21	27	24	12
6	36	42	54	48	24

Page 15 **Exercise 2M**

1. 33	**2.** 21	**3.** 12	**4.** 12	**5.** 13	**6.** 12
7. 121	**8.** 62	**9.** 16	**10.** 81	**11.** 339	**12.** 562
13. 243	**14.** 145	**15.** 257	**16.** 232		

Page 15   **Exercise 2E**

1. 257	**2.** 205	**3.** 1296	**4.** 726	**5.** 305	**6.** 1387
7. 5457	**8.** 1754	**9.** 5231	**10.** 698	**11.** 3214	**12.** 2234
13. 4009	**14.** 84	**15.** 23	**16.** 27	**17.** 23	

Page 16   **Exercise 3M**

1. 86 r 2	**2.** 178 r 3	**3.** 149 r 1	**4.** 54 r 2	**5.** 64 r 2	**6.** 41 r 6
7. 528 r 2	**8.** 3570 r 1	**9.** 582 r 5	**10.** 426 r 2	**11.** 501 r 5	**12.** 39 r 1
13. 65 r 7	**14.** 832 r 7	**15.** 14 285 r 4	**16.** 536 r 2	**17.** 286 r 5	**18.** 1110 r 8
19. 612	**20.** 12 080 r 3				

Page 17   **Exercise 3E**

1. 17	**2.** 14	**3.** 5	**4.** 34	**5.** 13	**6.** 26
7. 9	**8.** 12	**9.** 19	**10.** 7	**11.** 115	**12.** 1428
13. 55	**14.** (a) 2	(b) 6	(c) 5		

Page 18   **Check Yourself Sections 1.1 and 1.2**

1. (a) 2011	(b) 23 201	(c) 9500	**2.** (a) 60 234 (b) 8207
(c) 5587	(d) 7209	(e) 903	**3.** (a) 533 (b) 282
(c) 369	(d) 2206	(c) 975	**4.** (a) 63 (b) 518
(c) 1968	(d) 168	**5.** (a) $54 \div 6 = 9$	(b) $45 \div 5 = 9$ (c) $252 \div 7 = 36$
(d) $414 \div 9 = 46$	(e) $256 \div 4 = 64$	(f) $216 \div 8 = 27$	**6.** (a) 12 (b) 12

Page 19   **Exercise 1M**

1. 864	**2.** 672	**3.** 805	**4.** 1768	**5.** 612
6. 1170	**7.** 972	**8.** 1176	**9.** 900	**10.** 1672
11. 4324	**12.** 476	**13.** 3034	**14.** 1566	**15.** £1260
16. €5589	**17.** £7050			

Page 20   **Exercise 1E**

1. 3266	**2.** 3528	**3.** 12 614	**4.** 4890	**5.** 4992
6. 2844	**7.** 7587	**8.** 5192	**9.** 32 292	**10.** 3807
11. 69 012	**12.** 602 litres	**13.** 1050	**14.** 9744	**15.** 1848
16. 24×35	**17.** 13×425			

Page 22   **Exercise 2M**

1. (a) 482	(b) 54	**2.** 22	**3.** 24	**4.** 32
5. 27	**6.** 37	**7.** 31	**8.** 45	**9.** 14
10. 24	**11.** 23	**12.** 17	**13.** 61	

Page 22 **Exercise 2E**

1. 32 r 2	**2.** 34 r 5	**3.** 37	**4.** 44 r 8	**5.** 25
6. 47	**7.** 23 r 2	**8.** 23 r 2	**9.** 25	**10.** 12
11. 187	**12.** 36	**13.** 241	**14.** (a) 17	(b) 24
(c) 36	**15.** 1664	**16.** 35	**17.** 630 cm	**18.** 33

Page 24 **Exercise 1M**

1. 11	**2.** 1	**3.** –5	**4.** 12	**5.** 21
6. 2	**7.** 17	**8.** 24	**9.** 9	**10.** 30
11. 30	**12.** 25	**13.** 8	**14.** 5	**15.** 6
16. 8	**17.** 8	**18.** 3	**19.** 7	**20.** –2
21. –4	**22.** 14	**23.** 13	**24.** 0	**25.** 52
26. 11	**27.** 10	**28.** 20	**29.** 5	**30.** 5

31. (a) $4 \times 4 - 7 = 9$ (b) $20 - 3 \times 5 = 5$ (c) $24 \div 3 - 4 = 4$ (d) $(10 - 1) \times 4 = 36$
(e) $26 - (10 - 3) = 19$ (f) $36 \div (7 - 1) = 6$ (g) $(6 + 7) \times 5 = 65$ (h) $11 - 12 \div 2 = 5$
(i) $9 + 7 \times 3 = 30$ (j) $44 + (24 \div 2) = 56$ (k) $(3 \times 7) - 21 = 0$ (l) $48 \div 8 + 11 = 17$

Page 25 **Exercise 1E**

1. 15	**2.** 10	**3.** 5	**4.** 9	**5.** 11	**6.** 1
7. 7	**8.** 0	**9.** 8	**10.** 4	**11.** 0	**12.** 1
13. 18	**14.** 18	**15.** 12	**16.** 27	**17.** 8	**18.** 6
19. 1	**20.** 22	**21.** 9	**22.** 0	**23.** 5	**24.** 0
25. 20	**26.** 10	**27.** 16	**28.** 52	**29.** 40	**30.** 111
31. 51	**32.** 30	**33.** 11	**34.** 9	**35.** 28	**36.** 106
37. 54	**38.** 4	**39.** 4	**40.** 153	**41.** 59	**42.** 165
43. 85	**44.** 12	**45.** 33	**46.** 64	**47.** 67	**48.** 1172

Page 26 **Exercise 2M**

1. $(3 + 4) \times 5 = 35$ **2.** $6 + (9 \times 7) = 69$ **3.** $(7 \times 2) + 3 = 17$
4. $(9 + 12) \times 5 = 105$ **5.** $6 \times (8 - 2) = 36$ **6.** $(3 \times 8) - 6 = 18$
7. $(19 - 6) \times 3 = 39$ **8.** $27 - (9 \div 3) = 24$ **9.** $(51 \div 3) + 4 = 21$
10. $7 \times (24 - 5) = 133$ **11.** $(6 + 14) \div 2 = 10$ **12.** $(11 + 6) \times 4 = 68$
13. $(12 \times 8) - (9 \times 7) = 33$ **14.** $(8 \times 9) - (4 \times 7) = 44$ **15.** $(5 \times 6 - 4) \div 2 = 13$
16. $(81 \div 9) \times (12 - 4) = 72$ **17.** $(3 + 5) \times (9 - 7) = 16$ **18.** $(16 - 10) \div (18 \div 6) = 2$
19. $(6 + 7 - 1) \div 2 = 6$ **20.** $(5 + 7) \div 3 \times 0 = 0$

Page 26 **Exercise 2E**

1. $(4 + 8) \div 2 = 6$ **2.** $(5 + 2) \times 3 = 21$ **3.** $(7 + 2) \div 3 = 3$
4. $(9 - 4) + 2 = 7$ **5.** $(8 - 4) \times 5 = 20$ **6.** $(20 - 2) \div 3 = 6$
7. $(7 \times 4) + 2 = 30$ **8.** $(7 \times 6) - 22 = 20$ **9.** $(6 \div 3) \times 4 = 8$

10. $40 \div (8 - 3) = 8$
11. $(36 + 4) \div 8 = 5$
12. $(49 \div 7) \times 2 = 14$
13. $21 + 14 - 11 = 24$
14. $(16 \times 3) + 9 = 57$
15. $(12 + 16) \div 4 = 7$
16. $42 + 6 - 24 = 24$
17. $(18 - 13) \times 5 = 25$
18. $40 \div (16 - 6) = 4$
19. $(7 \times 8) - 6 = 50$
20. $(13 \times 4) - 8 = 44$
21. $4 \times (9 \div 3) = 12$
22. $7 \times (9 \div 3) = 21$
23. $(45 \div 3) - 4 = 11$
24. $(121 \div 11) \times 7 = 77$

Page 27   ***Exercise 3M***

1. (a) $8 + \dfrac{6}{2}$ (b) $\dfrac{10}{2} + 4$ (c) $12 - \dfrac{8}{2}$ (d) $\dfrac{10}{3 + 1}$ (e) $\dfrac{12 - 7}{2}$ (f) $\dfrac{10}{5} - 1$

2. (a) 2   (b) 8   (c) 3   (d) 3   (e) 2   (f) 2
  (g) 4   (h) 19   **3.** 4.175   **4.** 15.87   **5.** 3.18   **6.** 5.32
7. 2.31   **8.** 12.71   **9.** 0.5032   **10.** 9   **11.** 6.4   **12.** 0.28
13. 469.65   **14.** 14.01   **15.** 9.94   **16.** 9.084   **17.** 15.63   **18.** 0.56
19. 15.15   **20.** 11.44   **21.** 6.2   **22.** 5.34   **23.** 7.9   **24.** 35.64
25. 14.91   **26.** 0.09   **27.** 13.03   **28.** 4.913   **29.** 18.76   **30.** 4.6
31. 2.11   **32.** 2.7

Page 28   ***Exercise 3E***

1. (a) 5   (b) 8   (c) 4   (d) 3
2. (a) $17 - (4.2 \times 3) =$ (b) $28 \div (2.41 + 4.59) =$ **3.** 9.05   **4.** 11.36   **5.** 5.7
6. 12.4   **7.** 1.51   **8.** 4.68   **9.** 2.81   **10.** 4.07
11. 15   **12.** 2.4   **13.** 3.712   **14.** 8.4   **15.** 8.2695
16. 9.757   **17.** 5.98   **18.** 6.2   **19.** 17   **20.** 2.1
21. C/E, B/D, F/G   **22.** (a) $(9 - 3) \div (4 + 8) =$ (b) $30 \div (8 - 3) = + (4 \times 7) =$
23. 11.515   **24.** 3.2   **25.** 4.4   **26.** 6.4   **27.** 5.375
28. 17   **29.** 2.2   **30.** 1.6

Page 30   ***Check Yourself on Sections 1.3 and 1.4***

1. (a) 630   (b) 1701   (c) 13 272   **2.** (a) 23   (b) 24   **3.** (a) 5
  (b) 87   (c) 8   (d) 55   (e) 5   (f) 30   **4.** (a) 99
  (b) 15.9   (c) 8.61   (d) 1.07   (e) 9

Page 31   ***Exercise 1M***

1. (a) 1   (b) 24   (c) 30   (d) 17   **2.** 5   **3.** 36
4. 32   **5.** $2\frac{1}{2}$ **6.** 9   **7.** 45   **8.** 19   **9.** 30 000
10. 2.5   **11.** 81   **12.** -12 **13.** -3 **14.** 16   **15.** 2
16. $12\frac{1}{2}$ **17.** -4

Page 31 **Exercise 1E**

1. (a) 14   (b) 26   (c) 6   (d) 1.3   (e) 2   (f) 1.1
2. 3   **3.** 2000   **4.** 1.4   **5.** 5   **6.** -1 **7.** 10
8. (a) 48   (b) 7   (c) 2   (d) 9   **9.** 720   **10.** 5×7^2
11. $\dfrac{5}{11}$ **12.** 1440   **13.** 16

Page 32 **Exercise 2M**

1. 20, 25, 30, 35, 40   **2.** (a) 8, 10, 12, 14, 16   (b) 100, 96, 92, 88, 84
    (c) 10, 20, 40, 80, 160   (d) 64, 32, 16, 8, 4   **3.** (a) add 7
    (b) subtract 11   (c) add 0.2   (d) multiply by 2
4. (a) 47   (b) 3   (c) $25 - 51 - 103 - 207$
5. (a) 28   (b) 3   (c) $1 - 1 - 1 - 1$
6. (a) add $\dfrac{1}{2}$ (b) multiply by 2   (c) add 0.1
    (d) divide by 3   **7.** (b) 4, 12, 24, 40, 60, 84   **8.** add 2, multiply by 3 (many others)
9. -7 or less

Page 34 **Exercise 2E**

1. (a) 5, 10, 15, etc   (b) (e.g.) 0.1, 5.1, 10.1,...   (c) no
2. (a) 2, 5, 8, 11, 14, 17   (b) 10, 14, 18, 22, 26, 30, 34   (c) 40, 37, 34, 31, 28, 25
3. (a) 4, 9, 14, 19, 24   (b) 20, 17, 14, 11, 8   (c) 3, 6, 12, 24, 48
    (d) 1, 10, 100, 1000, 10 000   **4.** (a) $5 \times 999 = 4995$, $6 \times 999 = 5994$, $7 \times 999 = 6993$
    (b) $33333 \times 5 = 166\,665$, $333\,333 \times 5 = 1\,666\,665$ (c) $1\,666\,666\,665$
5. (a) $5^2 + 5 + 6 = 36$, $6^2 + 6 + 7 = 49$, $7^2 + 7 + 8 = 64$ (b) $12^2 + 12 + 13 = 169$
6. (a) $654\,321 \times 9 = 5\,888\,889$ (b) $= 788\,888\,889$
7. (a) $5 + 9 \times 1234 = 11111$ (b) $7 + 9 \times 123456 = 1111111$
8. (a) $6 \times 7 = 6 + 6 \times 6$ (b) $10 \times 11 = 10 + 10 \times 10$, $11 \times 12 = 11 + 11 \times 11$
9. $13 + 15 + 17 + 19 = 64 = 4^3$ etc   **10.** (a) 1, 7, 21, 35, 35, 21, 7, 1
    (b) 21, 28, 36   (c) 1, 2, 4, 8, 16, etc   (d) $512 (= 2^9)$

Page 37 **Check Yourself on Section 1.5**

1. (a) 17   (b) 8   (c) 37   (d) 8   (e) 1.3   **2.** (a) 29
    (b) 7, 17   (c) $6 \to 15 \to 33 \to 69$ **3.** (a) $\dfrac{1}{3}$ (b) 4×5^2 (c) 31
    (d) 6   (e) (i) ▯   (ii) ● ○ ● ○ ●

Page 38 **Exercise 1M**

1. (a) 44 cm   (b) 24 cm   (c) 62 cm   **2.** (a) 24 cm   (b) 24 cm
3. (a) 12 cm   (b) 11 cm   (c) 9 cm   **4.** (a) 12 cm   (b) 10 cm
    (c) 11 cm   **5.** (a) 28 cm   (b) 34 cm   (c) 44 cm   (d) 42 cm
6. (a) 28 cm   (b) 56 cm   (c) 24 cm   (d) 18 cm   **7.** 40 cm

Page 39   **Exercise 1E**

1. Missing numbers : 32, 22, 7, 9, 19.2, 14 (all cm)   **2.** (a) 32 m   (b) 16
3. 22 cm   **4.** 28 cm   **5.** 36 cm   **6.** 40 cm   **7.** 36 cm
8. 38 cm   **9.** 42 cm   **10.** 50 cm   **11.** 17 m   **12.** 36 cm

Page 41   **Exercise 2M**

1. (a) 77 cm^2 (b) 54 cm^2 (c) 24 cm^2 (d) 36 cm^2 **2.** (a) 10.5 cm^2
   (b) 23.8 cm^2 **3.** (a) 57 cm^2 (b) 94 cm^2 **4.** (a) 16 cm^2 (b) 49 cm^2
   (c) 36 cm^2 (d) 100 cm^2 **5.** 5 cm   **6.** (a) 200 cm × 150 cm   (b) 150

Page 42   **Exercise 2E**

1. (all cm^2)   (a) 50   (b) 43   (c) 120   (d) 119
   (e) 140   (f) 132   (g) 90   (h) 123   **2.** (a) 7 cm
   (b) 9 cm   (c) 9 cm   (d) 9.5 m   **3.** 8 cm   **4.** 28 cm
5. 48 m^2 **6.** 2700 cm^2 **7.** 3

Page 44   **Exercise 3M**

1. (all cm^2)   (a) 16   (b) 27   (c) 44   (d) $10\frac{1}{2}$

   (e) 80   (f) 54   (g) 35   (h) $22\frac{1}{2}$ **2.** (a) 40 m^2
   (b) 42 cm^2 (c) 80 mm^2 (d) 375 m^2 **3.** 6 cm^2 (b) 30 cm^2
   (c) 96 cm^2 (d) 12 cm^2 **4.** Missing numbers: 12 cm^2, 9 cm, 20 cm, 6 cm, 30 cm,
5. (a) 168 cm^2 (b) 90 cm^2 (c) 180 cm^2

Page 45   **Exercise 3E**

1. (a) 88 cm^2 (b) 109 cm^2 (c) 181 cm^2 (d) 63 cm^2 **3.** 99 m^2
4. 18 cm   **5.** 39 cm^2

Page 46   **Investigation**

Part D   Largest area is a square of side 8 cm
Part E   Square of side 25cm. Area is 625 cm^2.

Page 47   **Check Yourself on Section 1.6**

1. (a) 52 cm   (b) 50 m   (c) 62 cm   (d) 7 m   **2.** (a) 40 cm^2
   (b) 81 cm^2 (c) 92 cm^2 (d) 7 m   **3.** (a) 33 cm^2 (b) 28 m^2
   (c) 30 cm^2 (d) 132 cm^2 (e) 20 m

Page 48   **Mixed Review**

1. (a) 236 + 172   (b) 359 + 204   (c) 585 + 178   (d) 349 + 356   (e) 246 + 168
   (f) 559 + 294   2. (a) 50 – 43   (b) 46 – 38   (c) 86 + 52   (d) 316 – 253
   (e) 691 – 278   (f) 474 – 129   3. (a) $67 \times 2 = 134$ (b) $86 \times 4 = 344$
   (c) $57 \times 6 = 342$ (d) $39 \times 3 = 117$ (e) $239 \times 6 = 1434$ (f) $533 \times 4 = 2132$
4. Missing digits: (a) 5   (b) 2   (c) 6   (d) 5   (e) 4   (f) 8

5.

^{1}1	^{2}9		^{3}2	^{4}4
^{5}1	8		^{6}5	6
7		^{7}8	4	
	^{8}6	9		^{9}4
^{10}9	0		^{11}9	4

Part two

1. (a) 64 cm^2 (b) 42 cm^2
3. 224
4. (a) $5 \times 6 - 6 = 24$
   (b) $30 - 4 \times 7 = 2$
   (c) $36 \div 9 + 7 = 11$
   (d) $(12 - 7) \times 4 = 20$
   (e) $32 - (12 - 8) = 28$
   (f) $13 - 12 \div 2 = 7$
5. 9.52   6. 62.4
8. 7.7   9. 3.5
11. 4.07   12. 4.6

2.

	7	4	9	8
5	35	20	45	40
2	14	8	18	16
6	42	24	54	48
9	63	36	81	72

7. 4.6
10. 6.4
13. 15

	5	9	8	6	4
3	15	27	24	18	12
7	35	63	56	42	28
2	10	18	16	12	8
5	25	45	40	30	20
8	40	72	64	48	32

14. 10.65   15. 8.4   16. 3.2
17. (a) add 5   (b) multiply by 2   (c) take away 6   (d) add 0.2   (e) multiply by 3
   (f) multiply by 2 and then add 1
18. (a) 34 cm^2 (b) 85 cm^2
19. (a) 26 cm   (b) 48 cm
20. 1441
21. 5635 seconds = 93 minutes 55 seconds

Page 52   **Puzzles and Problems 1**

1. 41×32 2. 52×431 4. (a) black   (b) white   (c) 21st
   (d) 24th   5. 12
6. 11 tapes at £7.99 : £87.89
7.

E	C	A	D	B
D	B	E	C	A
C	A	D	B	E
B	E	C	A	D
A	D	B	E	C

8. Three on each side, etc!

Page 54   ***Mental Arithmetic Test 1***

1. 300   **2.** 6   **3.** 8043   **4.** $\frac{1}{4}$ **5.** 31   **6.** 54

7. 9   **8.** 8   **9.** 48   **10.** 16   **11.** 30%   **12.** 8 or 16

13. 36 m²   **14.** 7, 14, 21, etc   **15.** 14°C   **16.** 15   **17.** 9.05   **18.** 280

19. 120°   **20.** £1.58

Page 54   ***Mental Arithmetic Test 2***

1. 56   **2.** 5027   **3.** 184   **4.** 32   **5.** 30   **6.** 0.75

7. 14   **8.** 150 mm   **9.** 370   **10.** 3.4   **11.** 28   **12.** 81

13. 77%   **14.** 7.5   **15.** 60   **16.** 16°C   **17.** 0.3   **18.** £3.22

19. 46°   **20.** 6.25

Unit 2

Page 57 ***Exercise 1M***

1. (a) 3 (b) 4 and 7 **2.** (a) 6 (b) 5 (c) 6 **3.** (a) 3

(b) 2.5 (c) 12 **4.** (a) 10 (b) 20 **5.** 79p **6.** 13

7. (a) 26 (b) 27 (c) Nina by 1 **8.** 45 700 **9.** (a) 2 (b) 8

10. 165 cm **11.** 23 kg **12.** (a) 90 g (b) 205 g (c) 220 g (d) 193 g

Page 58 ***Exercise 1E***

1. (a) 6 (b) 6.5 **2.** (a) 14 (b) 16 (c) 14.8 **3.** 66 or 5

4. (a) 2 modes; 7 and 12 (b) 3, 8 and 12 **5.** 4.5; she wins **6.** −2° **7.** 3, 11

8. (a) False (b) Possible (c) Possible **9.** 3 **10.** (a) 6 (b) 14

11. (a) 11, 11, 16, 16, 15 (b) 15 **12.** 3

Page 61 ***Exercise 2M***

1. A: median = 7, range = 7   B: median = 4, range = 4   greater, greater, more

2. C: mean = 7, range = 11 D: mean = 9, range = 10

4. (a) Year 7: median = 4, range = 6 (b) Year 11: median = 3, range = 7

5. (a) Year 8: mean = 5.2, range = 5 (b) Year 9: mean = 4.7, range = 5

Page 62 ***Exercise 2E***

1. (a) mean = 4.7, range = 9 (b) mean = 6, range = 10

2. (a) 1.88 m (b) 0.34 m (c) 1.93 m (d) 0.14 m (e) Tipperton

3. (a) 71s (b) 8s (c) 78s (d) 12s (e) Helen

4. ALC mean = 7, range = 3; COMPH mean = 6, range = 13. ALC is more consistent although mean time is one minute longer

Page 64 ***Check Yourself on Section 2.1***

1. (a) 9 (b) 8.5 (c) 8 **2.** 37

3. Warriors: mean = 23.8 range = 14; Sabres: mean = 22.7 range = 12

Page 66 ***Exercise 1M***

2. (a) $\frac{12}{16}$ (b) $\frac{4}{20}$ (c) $\frac{10}{12}$ (d) $\frac{4}{5}$ (e) $\frac{15}{27}$ (f) $\frac{20}{35}$

(g) $\frac{9}{24}$ (h) $\frac{36}{60}$ (i) $\frac{21}{30}$ (j) $\frac{25}{40}$ (k) $\frac{20}{55}$ (l) $\frac{48}{60}$

(m) $\frac{4}{5}$ (n) $\frac{3}{5}$ (o) $\frac{4}{9}$ (p) $\frac{7}{10}$ **3.** (a) $\frac{3}{5}$ (b) $\frac{1}{3}$

(c) $\dfrac{3}{5}$ (d) $\dfrac{1}{5}$ (e) $\dfrac{4}{5}$ (f) $\dfrac{7}{9}$ (g) $\dfrac{2}{3}$ (h) $\dfrac{2}{3}$

(i) $\dfrac{2}{3}$ (j) $\dfrac{3}{5}$ (k) $\dfrac{7}{9}$ (l) $\dfrac{5}{6}$ (m) $\dfrac{4}{5}$ (n) $\dfrac{2}{7}$

(o) $\dfrac{3}{7}$ (p) $\dfrac{3}{4}$ (q) $\dfrac{2}{3}$ (r) $\dfrac{1}{4}$ (s) $\dfrac{7}{9}$ (t) $\dfrac{2}{3}$

(u) $\dfrac{3}{4}$ (v) $\dfrac{4}{7}$ (w) $\dfrac{3}{8}$ (x) $\dfrac{2}{3}$ (y) $\dfrac{5}{9}$

4. (a) $\dfrac{6}{10}$ (b) $\dfrac{5}{9}$ (c) $\dfrac{32}{40}$ (d) $\dfrac{20}{45}$

Page 67   ***Exercise 1E***

1. Water   **2.** Brazil   **3.** Rugby   **4.** Dublin   **5.** Shirt
6. Apricot

Page 68   ***Exercise 2M***

1. (a) 5   (b) 9   (c) 4   (d) 8   (e) 7
     (f) 6   (g) 9   (h) 5   **2.** (a) £7   (b) £14
3. (a) 5   (b) 25   **4.** (a) 3 cm   (b) £3   (c) 12 cm
     (d) 28 litres   (e) £9   (f) £8   (g) 25 kg   (h) 7 cm
     (i) 9 cm   (j) 17 kg   (k) 15 kg   (l) 20 m   (m) 70 litres
     (n) £8   (o) 9 kg   **5.** (a) 20 minutes   (b) 6 minutes   (c) 4 minutes
6. (a) 3   (b) 5   (c) 2   (d) 4   (e) 10
     (f) 4   (g) 8   (h) 3   (i) 5

Page 70   ***Exercise 2E***

1. (a) 7   (b) 28   **2.** (a) 9   (b) 27   **3.** (a) 15
     (b) 15   (c) 63   (d) 22   (e) 35   (f) 8
     (g) 32   (h) 40   **4.** 35   **5.** 21 litres   **6.** 72
7. PYRAMID   **8.** (a) 30 kg   (b) 72 cm   (c) £60   (d) £36
     (e) 150 kg   (f) 24 m   (g) 20 cm   (h) 48 m   (i) £148
9. £93   **10.** (a) 3   (b) 2   (c) 10   (d) 4
     (e) 20   (f) 40   **11.**   (c) 8 squares

Page 72   ***Exercise 3M***

1. $\dfrac{4}{7}$ **2.** $\dfrac{3}{4}$ **3.** $\dfrac{5}{8}$ **4.** $\dfrac{1}{5}$ **5.** $\dfrac{2}{9}$ **6.** $\dfrac{9}{10}$

7. $\dfrac{5}{9}$ **8.** $\dfrac{3}{25}$ **9.** $\dfrac{3}{7}$ **10.** $\dfrac{3}{4}$ **11.** $\dfrac{6}{7}$ **12.** $\dfrac{5}{9}$

13. (a) $\dfrac{1}{9}+\dfrac{6}{9}=\dfrac{7}{9}$ (b) $\dfrac{7}{8}-\dfrac{4}{8}=\dfrac{3}{8}$ (c) $\dfrac{14}{20}-\dfrac{9}{20}=\dfrac{5}{20}=\dfrac{1}{4}$ **14.** $\dfrac{7}{10}$ **15.** $\dfrac{1}{8}$

16. $\dfrac{1}{4}$ **17.** $\dfrac{1}{8}$ **18.** $\dfrac{7}{8}$ **19.** $\dfrac{3}{4}$ **20.** $\dfrac{9}{16}$ **21.** $\dfrac{1}{8}$

22. $\dfrac{9}{10}$ **23.** $\dfrac{7}{8}$ **24.** $\dfrac{1}{4}$ **25.** $\dfrac{1}{2}$ **26.** $\dfrac{1}{6}$ **27.** $\dfrac{6}{25}$

28. $\dfrac{3}{4}$ **29.** $\dfrac{1}{10}$

Page 73 **Exercise 3E**

2. (a) $\dfrac{5}{10}+\dfrac{2}{10}=\dfrac{7}{10}$ (b) $\dfrac{8}{12}+\dfrac{3}{12}=\dfrac{11}{12}$ (c) $\dfrac{21}{24}-\dfrac{16}{24}=\dfrac{5}{24}$ **3.** $\dfrac{17}{20}$ **4.** $\dfrac{11}{12}$

5. $\dfrac{5}{12}$ **6.** $\dfrac{2}{21}$ **7.** $\dfrac{31}{40}$ **8.** $\dfrac{5}{24}$ **9.** $\dfrac{11}{90}$

10. $\dfrac{39}{40}$ **11.** $\dfrac{43}{60}$ **12.** $\dfrac{59}{63}$ **13.** $\dfrac{29}{45}$ **14.** $\dfrac{1}{30}$

15. (a) $\dfrac{11}{12}$ (b) $\dfrac{3}{20}$ (c) $\dfrac{2}{15}$ **16.** (a) $\dfrac{8}{15}$ (b) $\dfrac{7}{15}$

17. $\dfrac{11}{15}$ m **18.** Many answers, eg. $\dfrac{1}{2}+\dfrac{4}{8},\dfrac{1}{5}+\dfrac{8}{10}$. etc.

Page 75 **Exercise 1M**

1. 0.7 **2.** 0.39 **3.** 0.5 **4.** 0.07 **5.** 0.9 **6.** 0.13

7. 0.25 **8.** 0.01 **9.** 0.41 **10.** 0.75 **11.** 0.35 **12.** $\dfrac{15}{100}=0.15$

13. $\dfrac{8}{10}=0.8$ **14.** $\dfrac{1}{4}=0.25$ **15.** $\dfrac{6}{10}=0.6$ **16.** $\dfrac{16}{100}=0.16$ **17.** 0.55 **18.** 0.4

19. 0.28 **20.** 0.75 **21.** 0.85 **22.** 0.92 **23.** 0.76 **24.** 0.75

25. 0.6 **26.** 0.25 **27.** Missing numbers: 0.4, $\dfrac{3}{100}$, 0.71, $\dfrac{9}{20}$, 0.02, $\dfrac{53}{100}$, 0.45

Page 76 **Exercise 1E**

1. 0.3, $\dfrac{9}{25}$, $\dfrac{8}{20}$ **2.** $\dfrac{3}{5}$, 0.7, $\dfrac{3}{4}$ **3.** 0.7, $\dfrac{12}{16}$, $\dfrac{4}{5}$ **4.** $\dfrac{1}{20}$, 0.15, $\dfrac{1}{5}$ **5.** 0.019

6. 0.008 **7.** 0.136 **8.** 0.75 **9.** 0.075 **10.** 0.028

11. 0.25 **12.** 0.178 **13.** 0.012 **14.** 0.0173

Page 76   **Exercise 2M**

1. $\frac{3}{10}$ 2. $\frac{7}{10}$ 3. $\frac{1}{100}$ 4. $\frac{9}{100}$ 5. $\frac{13}{100}$ 6. $\frac{51}{100}$

7. $\frac{69}{100}$ 8. $\frac{9}{10}$ 9. $\frac{23}{100}$ 10. $\frac{37}{100}$ 11. $\frac{89}{100}$ 12. $2\frac{3}{10}$

13. $4\frac{73}{100}$ 14. $5\frac{1}{100}$ 15. $6\frac{7}{10}$ 16. $\frac{4}{10}=\frac{2}{5}$ 17. $\frac{5}{100}=\frac{1}{20}$ 18. $\frac{8}{100}=\frac{2}{25}$

19. $\frac{12}{100}=\frac{3}{25}$ 20. $\frac{37}{100}$

Page 77   **Exercise 2E**

1. same amount   2. $\frac{4}{5}$ 3. $\frac{1}{20}$ 4. $\frac{2}{25}$ 5. $\frac{1}{4}$ 6. $\frac{6}{25}$

7. $\frac{1}{50}$ 8. $\frac{2}{5}$ 9. $\frac{8}{25}$ 10. $\frac{3}{20}$ 11. $\frac{9}{50}$ 12. $\frac{3}{4}$

13. $3\frac{1}{5}$ 14. $4\frac{1}{2}$ 15. $\frac{14}{25}$ 16. $6\frac{1}{25}$ 17. $7\frac{3}{25}$ 18. $3\frac{3}{4}$

19. $8\frac{3}{5}$ 20. $2\frac{19}{20}$ 21. $4\frac{9}{25}$

Page 77   **Exercise 3M**

1. (a) $\frac{2}{5}$ (b) $\frac{7}{100}$ (c) $\frac{11}{50}$ (d) $\frac{4}{5}$ (e) $\frac{1}{20}$ (f) $\frac{89}{100}$

(g) $\frac{1}{10}$ (h) $\frac{7}{25}$ (i) $\frac{1}{25}$ (j) $\frac{7}{20}$ 2. (a) 40%   (b) 45%

(c) $\frac{12}{100}=12\%$ (d) $\frac{55}{100}=55\%$ (e) $\frac{90}{100}=90\%$ (f) $\frac{38}{100}=38\%$ 3. (a) 85%   (b) 52%

(c) 92%   4. $\frac{7}{10}$ 5. $\frac{9}{25}$ 6. (a) $33\frac{1}{3}\%$ (b) 75%   (c) $66\frac{2}{3}\%$

(d) 12.5%   7. $\frac{37}{50},\frac{3}{4},\frac{39}{50}$ 8. 4%   9. 20%

Page 79   **Exercise 3E**

1. (a) $\frac{37}{100}=37\%$ (b) $\frac{17}{100}=17\%$ (c) $\frac{3}{100}=3\%$ (d) $\frac{40}{100}=40\%$ 2. (a) 0.29   (b) 0.52

(c) 0.8   (d) 0.06   (e) 0.03   (f) 0.13   (g) 1.3   (h) 2.4

3.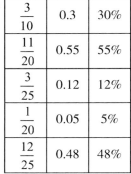

$\frac{3}{10}$	0.3	30%
$\frac{11}{20}$	0.55	55%
$\frac{3}{25}$	0.12	12%
$\frac{1}{20}$	0.05	5%
$\frac{12}{25}$	0.48	48%

4. Jack is higher by 2%

5. 15%

6. (a) MATHS IS NOT HARD
   (b) DECIMALS MAKE SENSE
   (c) I CAN SOLVE PROBLEMS

Page 80   Investigation – Escape

(a) 3 prisoners; 1, 4, 9   (b) 10 prisoners; 1, 4, 9, 16, 25, 36, 49, 64, 81, 100

Page 81   Check Yourself on Sections 2.2 and 2.3

1. (a) $\dfrac{7}{42}$ (b) $\dfrac{28}{36}$ (c) $\dfrac{2}{3}$ (d) $\dfrac{30}{42}$ (e) $\dfrac{49}{56}, \dfrac{63}{72}$

2. (a) 4   (b) 20   (c) 42   (d) 16

3. (a) $\dfrac{7}{9}$ (b) $\dfrac{29}{35}$ (c) $\dfrac{1}{12}$ (d) $\dfrac{13}{16}$

4. 40%, 0.4, $\dfrac{2}{5}$; 75%, 0.75, $\dfrac{3}{4}$; 5%, 0.05, $\dfrac{1}{20}$; 45%, 0.45, $\dfrac{9}{20}$

Page 82   Exercise 1M

1. EF̂G or GF̂E   **2.** BÂC or CÂB   **3.** PQ̂R or RQ̂P
4. AD̂C or CD̂A   **5.** WX̂Y or YX̂W   **6.** MN̂P or PN̂M
7. (a) 65°   (b) 115°   **8.** (a) 110°   (b) 55°   (c) 110°   (d) 125°
9. (a) 68°   (b) 63°   **10.** (a) 88°   (b) 138°   **11.** (a) 41°   (b) 100°
   (c) 94°   **12.** (a) 33°   (b) 92°   (c) 46°

Page 83   Exercise 1E [Apologies: The diagram shown is not accurate!]

1. 20°	**2.** 40°	**3.** 60°	**4.** 72°	**5.** 10°	**6.** 45°
7. 65°	**8.** 80°	**9.** 36°	**10.** 23°	**11.** 14°	**12.** 28°
13. 126°	**14.** 135°	**15.** 170°	**16.** 6°	**17.** 30°	**18.** 174°
19. 166°	**20.** 160°	**21.** 157°	**22.** 150°	**23.** 144°	**24.** 53°
25. 115°	**26.** 155°	**27.** 97°	**28.** 108°	**29.** 120°	**30.** 127°
31. 25°	**32.** 83°	**33.** 91°	**34.** 107°	**35.** 140°	**36.** 54°
37. 73°	**38.** 89°	**39.** 152°	**40.** 100°		

Page 84   Exercise 2M

1. 50°	**2.** 50°	**3.** 35°	**4.** 46°	**5.** 37°	**6.** 120°
7. (a) 47°	(b) 95°	**8.** (a) 108°	(b) 36°	**9.** (a) 76°	(b) 127°
(c) 93°	**10.** (a) 68°	(b) 127°	(c) 93°		

Page 86   Exercise 3M

1. T	**2.** T	**3.** F	**4.** F	**5.** T	**6.** T
7. F	**8.** F	**9.** T	**10.** T	**11.** T	**12.** T
13. T	**14.** T	**15.** T	**16.** F	**17.** F	**18.** F

Page 87   **Exercise 3E**

A = acute, O = obtuse, R = reflex, RA = right angle

1. A	**2.** RA	**3.** A	**4.** A	**5.** O	**6.** R
7. O	**8.** A	**9.** O	**10.** R	**11.** O	**12.** R
13. RA	**14.** R	**15.** O	**16.** A	**17.** A	**18.** R

Page 87   **Exercise 4M**

1. 40°   **2.** 130°   **3.** 51°   **4.** 60°   **5.** 25°   **6.** 52°
7. 137°   **8.** 60°   **9.** 42°   **10.** j = 125°, k = 55°   **11.** l = 104°, m = 76°
12. n = 57°   **13.** 93°   **14.** 153°   **15.** r = 153°, s = 153°, t = 27°
16. u = 90°, v = 90°, w =90°

Page 88   **Exercise 4E**

1. a = 60°   **2.** b = 40°   **3.** c = 75°   **4.** d = 105°   **5.** e = 88°
6. f = 80°   **7.** g = 47°   **8.** h = 54°   **9.** i = 33°   **10.** j = 47°
11. k = 60°, 2k = 120°, 3k = 180°   **12.** m = 25°, 3m = 75°

Page 90   **Exercise 5M**

1. 65°   **2.** 45°   **3.** 17°   **4.** d = 60°, e = 120°   **5.** 39°
6. g = 84°, h = 96°   **7.** 110°   **8.** j = 60°, k = 60°   **9.** 66°   **10.** 105°
11. 86°   **12.** 66°   **13.** q = 50°, r = 54°, s = 126°   **14.** 120°
15. u = 71°, v = 152°   **16.** 162°

Page 91   **Exercise 5E**

1. a = 48°   **2.** b = 70°, c = 40°   **3.** d = 45°   **4.** e = 55°   **5.** f = 60°
6. g = 82°, h = 16°   **7.** i = 72°   **8.** j = 65°, k = 65°, l = 50°   **9.** m = 28°
10. n = 286°   **11.** p = 62°, q = 56°   **12.** r = 38°, s = 109°   **13.** 128°
14. 70°   **15.** slab B

Page 92   **Check Yourself on Section 2.4**

1. (a) 85°   (b) 30°   (c) 100°   **2.** (a) 62°   (b) 115°
3. (a) 40° ± 5°   (b) 75° ± 5°   (c) 155° ± 5°   **4.** (a) true   (b) false
   (c) true   **5.** (a) 65°   (b) 125°   (c) $\widehat{XWY} = 100°$, $\widehat{VWX} = 80°$
6. (a) 28°   (b) 102°   (c) $\widehat{PRQ} = 64°$, $\widehat{PRS} = 116°$

Page 95   **Exercise 1M**

1. $N + 3$ **2.** $d - 9$ **3.** $2x$ **4.** $y + 25$ **5.** $2k - 8$
6. $3M - 4$ **7.** $25p$ **8.** $2w + 15$ **9.** $10q - 8$ **10.** $3b + 8$
11. $p = 4y$ **12.** $p = 3a$ **13.** $p = 5m$ **14.** $p = 8h$ **15.** $p = 2x + 2y$
16. $p = 2w + 6$ **17.** $p = 2b + c$

Page 96   **Exercise 1E**

1. $b + c - m$
2. $2x + y$
3. $Q + 8 - P$
4. $3s - w$
5. $a + b + c - 8$
6. $4x - y + 5$
7. $g - f + n$
8. $2y + 3w - x$
9. $6m + 3n$
10. $5q - 3p + 4m$
11. $5x$
12. $y + 20$
13. $w - 9$
14. $3m$
15. $4x + 45$
16. $n + 4$

Page 98   **Exercise 2M**

1. $8a$
2. $4x$
3. $4a + 3b$
4. $6c - 4d$
5. $4d$
6. $3x + 2$
7. $9y$
8. $2h$
9. $3w$
10. y
11. $7x + y$
12. $9m$
13. $7y$
14. $6m + 5n$
15. $4x + 6$
16. $13b$
17. $12t$
18. p
19. $25n$
20. $6a - 5$
21. $8x + 2$
22. $30h$
23. $9 - 7x$
24. $8b - 4$
25. $7a + 6$
26. $6c$
27. $12y - 12$
28. $11y$

Page 98   **Exercise 2E**

1. $6a + 7b$
2. $9x + 7y$
3. $3x + 2y$
4. $3m + 8n$
5. $7a + 9$
6. $2a + 7b$
7. $3x + 2$
8. $9p + 5q$
9. $8x + 2$
10. $6a + 10b$
11. $12m + 1$
12. $2h + 25$
13. $12m + 6n$
14. $6p + 3q$
15. $9x + 4$
16. $8x + 3y + 6$
17. $4a + 3b + 4c$
18. $3w + 8$
19. $2a + 15$
20. $y + 3$
21. $6a + 12c$
22. $9p + 2q$
23. $7m + 2n + 4$
24. $14x + 8$
25. (a) $10x + 9$
(b) $12m + 11n + 6$
(c) $9a + 14b + 13$
26. (b) and (c)

Page 100   **Exercise 3M**

3. (a) $xy = yx, x + y = y + x$
4. (a) $n + n = 2 \times n, n \times n = n^2$
6. $bc + a^2$

Page 101   **Exercise 3E**

1. true
2. true
3. false
4. true
5. true
6. false
7. true
8. false
9. false
10. false
11. true
12. false
13. (a) $x = 80 - y$ (b) $p = 30 + q$ (c) $a = \dfrac{20}{b}$ (d) $n = 50 - m$ (e) $x = \dfrac{100}{w}$ (f) $n = \dfrac{e}{m}$
14. (a) 1 (b) a (c) n (d) 6

Page 101   **Investigation – Number walls**

Part A: Largest total obtained by putting largest numbers in the middle of the base, smallest numbers at either end.

Part D: Pupils should be encouraged (and helped) to use algebra.

With 3 bricks: Top brick $= a + 2b + c$

with 4 bricks: Top brick $= a + 3b + 3c + d$

with 5 bricks: Top brick $= a + 4b + 6c + 4d + e$

Pascal's triangle can be seen in the coefficients.

Page 103   **Exercise 4M**

1. 18	**2.** 40	**3.** 46	**4.** 47	**5.** 325	**6.** 28
7. (a) 50	(b) 122	(c) 43	**8.** 75		

Page 104   **Exercise 4E**

1. 17	**2.** 15	**3.** 37	**4.** 9	**5.** 6	**6.** 32
7. 28	**8.** 9	**9.** 7	**10.** 13	**11.** 2	**12.** 25
13. 30	**14.** 16	**15.** 72	**16.** 80	**17.** 50	**18.** 54
19. 55	**20.** 15				

Page 105   **Exercise 5M**

1. $\square = 8$	**2.** $\bigcirc = 5$	**3.** $\bigcirc = 12$	**4.** $\square = 4$	**5.** $\triangle = 3$	**6.** $\triangle = 4$
7. $\square = 12$	**8.** $\triangle = 10$	**9.** $\triangle = 14$	**10.** $\square = 8$	**11.** $\bigcirc = 9$	**12.** $\bigcirc = 5$

Page 106   **Exercise 5E**

1. $\square = \triangle = 5$ **2.** $\square = 2, \bigcirc = 4$ **3.** $\bigcirc = 3\frac{1}{2} = \triangle$ **4.** $\triangle = 3, \bigcirc = 6$ **5.** $\square = \triangle = 4$
6. $\triangle = 3, \bigcirc = 2$ **7.** $\bigcirc = 2, \square = 4$ **8.** $\triangle = 10, \square = 5$ **9.** $\bigcirc = 10, \square = 0$ **10.** $\triangle = 3, \bigcirc = 0$
11. $\triangle = 3, \bigcirc = 3$ **12.** $\triangle = 5, \square = 5$ **13.** $\square = 2, \bigcirc = 6$ **14.** $\square = 4, \triangle = 8$ **15.** $\triangle = 4, \bigcirc = 4$
16. $\diamondsuit = 12$

Page 107   **Check Yourself on Section 2.5**

1. (a) $4x$ (b) $n - 6$ (c) $2w + 24$ **2.** (a) $2m + 9n$ (b) $7y$ (c) $4p + 6$
   (d) $2a + 2b$ **3.** (a) 645   (b) 33   (c) 6   **4.** (a) $\square = 8$ (b) $\square = 12, \bigcirc = 3$

Page 108   **Unit 2 Mixed Review Part one**

1. (a) $\frac{3}{4}$ (b) $\frac{6}{7}$ (c) $\frac{18}{19}$ (d) $\frac{3}{8}$ **2.** (a) $\frac{4}{5}$ (b) 9

(c) $\frac{1}{4}$ **3.** (a) true   (b) false   (c) true   **4.** (a) $2x + 2y$ (b) $3n + 16$

6. (a) $8w + 3y$ (b) $5p + 6q$ (c) $2m + 2$ **7.** $y, 9.5g, x$ **8.** $\frac{9}{10}$ **9.** $\frac{7}{9}$

10. $\frac{3}{4}$ **11.** (a) $15°$ (b) $40°$ (c) $35°$ (d) $67°$ **12.** (a) 6

(b) 6   (c) 7   (d) 14   **13.** C   **14.** $74°$ **15.** 5, 11

Page 110   **Part two**

1.

$\frac{4}{25}$	0.16	16%
$\frac{7}{10}$	0.7	70%
$\frac{1}{4}$	0.25	25%

2. (a) $2n - 8$ (b) $3p + r$ **3.** $\frac{3}{5}$ of £75   **4.** d **5.** 6

6. $(4.9 - 5)$cm   **7.** (b) AB = 4.5 cm   **8.** (a) $2a + b + c$
   (b) $2a, a, 3a$ (c) $3m + n, 2m + 4n, 5m + 5n$ **9.** £107
10. (a) $30°$ (b) $105°$ (c) 8 cm   (d) 70 mm
   (e) 3   (f) $180°$ **11.** (a) $\frac{4}{9}$ (b) $\frac{13}{20}$

(c) $\dfrac{13}{40}$ **12.** Sefton   **13.** 6   **14.** (a) mean = 4, range = 9   (b) mean = 6, range = 8

15. (a) $6n + 3$ (b) C and D (c) $4n$ (d) $13n + 8$

*Page 113   **Puzzles and Problems 2   Hidden Words***

1. The horse is off and running.   **2.** You are the real top banana.   **3.** Anyone need a calculator?
4. Elvis was out of this world.   **5.** Most spiders eat raw flies.

*Page 116   **A long time ago! 2***

2. (a) 1472   (b) 2562   (c) 4144   (d) 38484   (e) 225568   (f) 4791773
   (g) 39720   (h) 82449

*Page 117   **Mental Arithmetic Test 1***

1. 300	**2.** 49 m^2	**3.** 80	**4.** 2000 cm	**5.** 16	**6.** 33p
7. 40	**8.** £4	**9.** 33 euros	**10.** 25 cm^2	**11.** 7	**12.** 0.55
13. 6	**14.** 135	**15.** 60°	**16.** 38 m	**17.** 165	**18.** 40
19. 86°	**20.** £500 000				

*Page 117   **Mental Arithmetic Test 2***

1. 0.03   **2.** 6   **3.** £11   **4.** £40   **5.** false   **6.** 11
7. 1, 2, 4, 8   **8.** 1.80 m   **9.** 0.7   **10.** 0.75   **11.** 51   **12.** 58%
13. −16°C   **14.** 402 012   **15.** 9   **16.** 20, 20, 2, 2, 1 or 10, 10, 10, 10, 5
17. $2\frac{1}{2}$ hours   **18.** 82   **19.** £2.31   **20.** 16

Unit 3

Page 119   **Exercise 1M**

1. C(4, 4)   D(1, 2)   E(7, 3)   F(3, 0)   G(2, 1)   H(0, 3)
  I(6, 5)   **2.** (a) (4, 8)   (b) (7, 4)   (c) (6, 7)   (d) (3, 4)   (e) (8, 4)
  (f) (5, 2)   **3.** (a) Hand grenade area   (b) Parachute drop zone   (c) Secret caves
  (d) Hospital C   (e) Interrogation centre   (f) Helicopter pad   (g) Hospital B
  (h) Look out point

Page 120   **Exercise 1E**

¹P	A	²P	E	³R		⁴F	A	R	
L		I		E		O			
⁵A	O	L		⁶A	U	R	A	L	
S		O		D		M			
T		⁷T	R	I	B	U	T	E	
E			N		L				
⁸R	E	⁹P	U	G	N	A	N	¹⁰T	
E		A						A	
¹¹D	E	R		¹²B	A	C	O	N	

Page 123   **Exercise 2E**

1. (a) (7, 7), (4, 6)   (b) (5, 11), (3, 10)   (c) (7, 3) (4, 2)
  (d) (9, 0), (9, 2)   (e) (11, 7), $(10\frac{1}{2}, 9\frac{1}{2})$ **2.** (a) (1, 1)
  (b) (6, 5)   (c) (6, 2)   **3.** (a) (4, 2)
  (b) (8, 8)   (c) (3, 10)   **4.** P: (3, 6), (7, 2), (1, 2)
  Q: (12, 4), (8, 6), (12, 12)   **5.** (a) (– 4, 0)   (b) (1, 0)
  (c) (3, 1)   (d) (2, 1)
6. (4, 3), (1, 5), (3, 1), (2, 7), (5, 6), (0, 2), (0, 4), (1, 4) (1, 6), (4, 2), (4, 4), (5, 4)
7. (a) (7, 3), (1, 5), (5, 1), (3, 7), (5, 3), (3, 5), (8, 0), (0, 8) etc
  (b) Any points on the line x + y = 8

Page 126   **Exercise 1M**

1. (a) 495   (b) 1075   (c) 666   **2.** (a) 1044   (b) 1134   (c) 7488
  (d) 6624   (e) 729   (f) 7712   **3.** (b) remainder 2   **4.** 32
5. 34   **6.** 37   **7.** (a) 544   (b) 325   (c) 24   (d) 1210
8. £9.90   **9.** 65p   **10.** 759

Page 126   **Exercise 1E**

1. 22 r 3   **2.** 37 r 2   **3.** 42 r 7   **4.** 31 r 1   **5.** 32 r 19   **6.** 15 r 6
7. £43.68   **8.** 37   **9.** £13.95   **10.** 23 × 54   **11.** 13   **12.** 14, 24p over

13. £27 **14.** 37 **15.** 3306 **16.** 26 and 2 left over

17. No. We need 13 more chairs **18.** £24480

Page 128 **Exercise 1M**

1. 3.2 cm **2.** (a) 2.3 cm (b) 2.4 cm (c) 2.8 cm (d) 6.5 cm (e) 3.4 cm

3. (a) 3.1 (b) 7.9 (c) 5.4 (d) 11.3 (e) 211.7 **4.** (a) 0.4

(b) 0.7 (c) 0.5 (d) 1.2 (e) 2.3 (f) 2.9 (g) 3.1

5. (a) 0.5 (b) 1.5 (c) 2.7 (d) 2.3 (e) 0.6 (f) 1.9

(g) 1.1 (h) 3.5 **6.** (a) $\frac{7}{10}$ (b) 10 (c) 5 (d) $\frac{4}{10}$

(e) $\frac{1}{100}$ (f) $\frac{4}{100}$ (g) $\frac{3}{10}$ (h) 4 (i) 30 (j) $\frac{7}{100}$

(k) 400 (l) $\frac{6}{100}$ **7.** (a) 0.6, 0.7 (b) 0.9, 1.1 (c) 1.6, 2.0 (d) 1.1, 1.3

(e) 1.0, 0.9 **8.** (a) 1.9 (b) 1 (c) 2.9 (d) 3.6 (e) 4.8

(f) 6.8 (g) 0.4 (h) 3.9 (i) 3.4 (j) 0.8 (k) 13.1

(l) 1 **9.** (a) seven point five two (b) six point two three seven

(c) eleven point nought four (d) sixty point six five (e) five pounds sixty-five

(f) Three pounds five pence (g) six point three two four (h) fifty pence

Page 130 **Exercise 1E**

1. T **2.** T **3.** T **4.** T **5.** T **6.** F

7. F **8.** F **9.** T **10.** F **11.** T **12.** T

13. T **14.** T **15.** T **16.** T

18. 7 is $\frac{7}{100}$ ths, 2 is $\frac{2}{10}$ ths, 1 is $\frac{1}{1000}$ th

19. 3 is $\frac{3}{10}$ ths, 6 is $\frac{6}{1000}$ ths, 8 is $\frac{8}{100}$ ths

20. (a) 0.3 (b) 0.07 (c) 0.11 (d) 0.004 (e) 0.16 (f) 0.016

21. (a) +0.4 (b) +0.005 (c) −0.2 (d) −0.06

Page 131 **Exercise 2M**

1. 0.12, 0.21, 0.31 **2.** 0.04, 0.35, 0.4 **3.** 0.67, 0.672, 0.7

4. 0.045, 0.05, 0.07 **5.** 0.089, 0.09, 0.1 **6.** 0.57, 0.705, 0.75

7. 0.041, 0.14, 0.41 **8.** 0.8, 0.809, 0.81 **9.** 0.006, 0.059, 0.6

10. 0.143, 0.15, 0.2 **11.** 0.04, 0.14, 0.2, 0.53 **12.** 0.12, 0.21, 1.12, 1.2

13. 0.08, 0.75, 2.03, 2.3 **14.** 0.26, 0.3, 0.602, 0.62 **15.** 0.5, 1.003, 1.03, 1.3

16. 0.709, 0.79, 0.792, 0.97 **17.** 52 cm, 152 cm, 5.2 m **18.** 75p, £0.8, £1.20

19. 200 m, $\frac{1}{2}$ km, 0.55 km **20.** 0.1 cm, 1.2 mm, 2 mm **21.** My teacher is ...

22. (a) 3.37 (b) 14.9 (c) 0.941 **23.** (a) 11.26 (b) 1.304 (c) 0.392

24. (a) 3.143 (b) 2.719 (c) 1.415 **25.** (a) £0.11 (b) £0.02 (c) £0.05

(d) £0.10 (e) £0.20 (f) £0.50

Page 132   *Exercise 2E*

1. 46	**2.** 2.6	**3.** 14.8	**4.** 15.2	**5.** 0.2	**6.** 3.2
7. 7	**8.** 5.2	**9.** 3.14	**10.** 0.02	**11.** 1.02	**12.** 0.8
13. 0.24	**14.** 120	**15.** 1.8	**16.** 16	**17.** 88	**18.** 4.35
19. 2.75	**20.** 3.55	**21.** 0.16	**22.** 72.5	**23.** 18.3	**24.** 3.13

Page 133   *Exercise 3M*

1. 7.8	**2.** 1.3	**3.** 8.5	**4.** 20.0	**5.** 15.1	**6.** 23.4
7. 16.5	**8.** 1.5	**9.** 4.2	**10.** 3.7	**11.** 4.7	**12.** 5.3
13. 5.26	**14.** 7.27	**15.** 16.59	**16.** 2.128	**17.** 13.045	**18.** 40.554
19. 21.67	**20.** 12.45	**21.** 465.601	**22.** 44.321	**23.** 13.852	**24.** 19.77
25. 15.6	**26.** 24.4	**27.** 51.9	**28.** 5.3	**29.** 2.41	**30.** 19.78
31. 88.73	**32.** 1.556	**33.** 24.084	**34.** 1.728	**35.** 0.986	**36.** 8.26

37. 7.82 + 1.45 = 9.27   **38.** 3.65 + 0.25 = 3.90   **39.** 5.37 + 3.54 = 8.91

40. 8.27 + 0.74 = 9.01   **41.** 6.86 + 2.17 = 9.03   **42.** 6.95 + 2.26 = 9.21

Page 134   *Exercise 3E*

1. 1.61m	**2.** 7.55m	**3.** £1	**4.** £1, 50p, 20p, 5p, 2p, 1p	**5.** £36.10
6. £9.54	**7.** £12.37	**8.** £1, 20p, 10p, 5p, 2p	**9.** £17.30	**10.** £3.86

11. 8.56 − 4.83 = 3.73   **12.** 4.07 + 4.96 = 9.03   **13.** 3.176 − 2.428 = 0.748

14. 8.78 + 0.88 = 9.66   **15.** 5.92 − 2.26 = 3.66   **16.** 2.457 + 4.348 = 6.805

17. 0.01	**18.** 0.002	**19.** (a) 1.272	(b) 9.012	(c) 11.819	(d). 8.678
		(e) 6.532	(f) 41.04	(g) 0.273	(h) 0.05	(i) 11.612	**20.** RELATION

Page 135   ***Top Banana***

1. £11.70   **2.** 250 points   **3.** £12.50   **4.** £0.80   **5.** spent £367.38   8000 points

Page 137   *Exercise 1M*

1. 42.3	**2.** 56.3	**3.** 42.7	**4.** 463	**5.** 0.75	**6.** 0.63
7. 1147	**8.** 10 700	**9.** 633	**10.** 71.4	**11.** 636	**12.** 81.42
13. 7100	**14.** 8900	**15.** 1200	**16.** 130	**17.** 7000	**18.** 92 000
19. 70	**20.** 50 000	**21.** 100	**22.** 5.5	**23.** 0.052	**24.** 180
25. 1000	**26.** 400	**27.** 1	**28.** 0.117	**29.** 0.002	**30.** F
31. 5.72	**32.** 8.92	**33.** 0.53	**34.** 0.471	**35.** 1.412	**36.** 1.93
37. 15.18	**38.** 0.047	**39.** 0.0252	**40.** 0.063	**41.** 0.472	**42.** 0.0279
43. 0.0062	**44.** 1.987	**45.** 4.7	**46.** 0.416		

Page 137   ***Exercise 1E***

1. 1000	**2.** 100	**3.** 0.032	**4.** 0.17	**5.** 1	**6.** 100
7. 1000	**8.** 6.54	**9.** 10	**10.** 1	**11.** 1000	**12.** 100
13. 41.4	**14.** 63.1	**15.** 0.5	**16.** 63	**17.** 4.74	**18.** 0.0897
19. 0.0542	**20.** 6300	**21.** 470	**22.** 8400	**23.** 0.007	**24.** 0.62
25. 47.3	**26.** 1	**27.** 0.47	**28.** 4700	**29.** 47, 4700, 470	

30. 60, 6, 60   **31.** 5.75, 0.575, 575   **32.** 8.2, 82, 0.82, 0.082

33. 9.5, 950, 95, 9.5   **34.** 730, 7300, 7.3, 73   **35.** 40, 0.4, 0.04, 0.4

36. 860, 8600, 86, 8.6   **37.** NUMBERS

Page 139   ***Exercise 2M***

1. 10.2	**2.** 6.9	**3.** 14.8	**4.** 28.0	**5.** 36.78	**6.** 71.54
7. 42.72	**8.** 11.61	**9.** 4.41	**10.** 8.712	**11.** 0.666	**12.** 56.5
13. 68	**14.** 0.37	**15.** 13.32	**16.** 92.4	**17.** (a) 1.2	(b) 7
(c) 0.4	(d) 0.2	(e) 0.5	(f) 0.02	**18.** £11.70	**19.** £21.90

20. 6.75 kg

Page 140   ***Exercise 2E***

1. (a) 25.4   (b) 6.48   (c) 10.15   (d) 12   (e) 510

2. (a) 1.1, 4.4, 44, 0.44   (b) 0.4, 2.8, 8.4, 84   (c) 1.5, 7.5, 22.5, 2250

(d) 0.04, 0.32, 32, 16   **3.** £12.78   **4.** £119.96   **5.** £9.52   **6.** £13.77

7. £12.50   **8.** £62.10   **9.** 14.08 pints   **10.** (a) £116   (b) £116 000

Page 141   ***Exercise 3M***

1. 4.21	**2.** 34.2	**3.** 4.63	**4.** 0.712	**5.** 47.2	**6.** 6.31
7. 6.24	**8.** 54.14	**9.** 1.34	**10.** £1.52		

11.

¹7	²6	³1	⁴2	⁵4
⁶2	0 ⁷8		⁸4	2
	⁹1	1 ¹⁰6		5
¹¹1		¹²3	¹³8	
¹⁴9	¹⁵7 3		¹⁶5	¹⁷3
¹⁸1	5	¹⁹1	0	2

Page 142   ***Exercise 3E***

1. 5.63 cm   **2.** £8.47   **3.** (a) 2.24   (b) 2.2525   (c) 1.5125

(d) 0.205   (e) 3.4   (f) 2.75   **4.** 0.928 kg   **5.** £3.73

6. 5.64 litres   **7.** 16   **8.** £0.99   **9.** 0.26 m   **10.** 25 g

Page 143   **Operator squares**

1.

32	÷	4	→	8
+	■	×	■	
40	×	7	→	280
↓	■	↓	■	
72	–	28	→	44

2.

18	×	5	→	90
–	■	+	■	
7	×	6	→	42
↓	■	↓	■	
11	–	11	→	0

3.

25	+	64	→	89
×	■	+	■	
6	×	17	→	102
↓	■	↓	■	
150	–	81	→	69

4.

35	×	10	→	350
–	■	÷	■	
0.2	×	100	→	20
↓	■	↓	■	
34.8	+	0.1	→	34.9

5.

38	×	8	→	304
÷	■	×	■	
2	×	14	→	28
↓	■	↓	■	
19	+	112	→	131

6.

2106	–	574	→	1532
÷	■	+	■	
9	×	25	→	225
↓	■	↓	■	
234	+	599	→	833

7.

10	×	0.1	→	1
÷	■	×	■	
4	÷	16	→	0.25
↓	■	↓	■	
2.5	+	1.6	→	4.1

8.

19.6	÷	7	→	2.8
×	■	+	■	
0.1	×	10	→	1
↓	■	↓	■	
1.96	+	17	→	18.96

9.

8.42	–	0.2	→	8.22
×	■	×	■	
100	×	12	→	1200
↓	■	↓	■	
842	+	2.4	→	844.4

10.

20	÷	100	→	0.2
×	■	÷	■	
22	×	200	→	4400
↓	■	↓	■	
440	×	0.5	→	220

11.

1.22	×	3	→	3.66
+	■	–	■	
3.78	+	0.2	→	3.98
↓	■	↓	■	
5	+	2.8	→	7.8

12.

324	+	578	→	902
÷	■	–	■	
9	×	52	→	468
↓	■	↓	■	
36	+	526	→	562

Page 144   **Exercise 1M**

1. Prime numbers: 2, 3, 5, 7, 11, 13, 17, 19, 23, 29, 31, 37, 41, 43, 47, 53, 59, 61, 67, 71, 73, 79, 83, 89, 97

Page 145   **Exercise 1E**

1. (a) 7   (b) 19   (c) 37   (d) 89   **2.** 25

3. 2 + 3 = 5,   2 + 5 = 7, 2 + 11 = 13 (+ many others)   **4.** One   **5.** 24

6. 19 and 23, 43 and 47, 79 and 83   **7.** 3 and 19, 5 and 17   **8.** (a) 11, 31, 41, 61, 71

  (b) 7, 17, 37, 47, 67, 97   (c) divisible by 5   **9.** True   **10.** 48 cm

11. 3 + 5 + 11 = 19 (+ others)   **12.** 103, 151, 293, 1999

Page 146   **Exercise 2M**

1. 1, 2, 3, 6   **2.** 1, 2, 4   **3.** 1, 2, 5, 10   **4.** 1, 7   **5.** 1, 3, 5, 15

6. 1, 2, 3, 6, 9, 18   **7.** 1, 2, 3, 4, 6, 8, 12, 24   **8.** 1, 3, 7, 21   **9.** 1, 2, 3, 4, 6, 9, 12, 18, 36

10. 1, 2, 4, 5, 8, 10, 20, 40   **11.** 1, 2, 4, 8, 16, 32   **12.** 1, 31

13. 1, 2, 3, 4, 5, 6, 10, 12, 15, 20, 30, 60   **14.** 1, 3, 7, 9, 21, 63

15. 1, 5, 17, 85   **16.** 6, 8   **17.** 18, 12

18. (a)

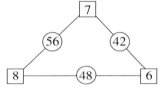

(b)

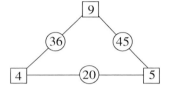

(c)

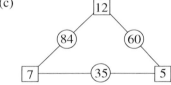

(d)

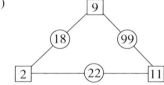

Page 147   **Exercise 2E**

1. (a) 1, 2, 5, 10, 25, 50   (b) 1, 2, 4, 11, 22, 44   (c) 1, 2, 4, 5, 10, 20, 25, 50, 100   (d) 1, 29

2. prime factors are $2 \times 2 \times 3 \times 3$ **3.** $2 \times 2 \times 7$ **4.** $2 \times 2 \times 2 \times 2 \times 2$ **5.** 2×17

6. $3 \times 3 \times 3 \times 3$ **7.** $2 \times 2 \times 3 \times 7$ **8.** $2 \times 2 \times 2 \times 3 \times 3 \times 3$

9. $2 \times 3 \times 7 \times 7$ **10.** $2 \times 2 \times 2 \times 5 \times 5$ **11.** $2 \times 2 \times 3 \times 5 \times 5 \times 5$

12. $2 \times 2 \times 2 \times 2 \times 2 \times 7 \times 11$ **13.** $2 \times 2 \times 3 \times 5 \times 7 \times 11$ **14.** $3 \times 5 \times 5 \times 7 \times 11 \times 17$

15. 4 (factors 1, 2, 4)   **16.** (a) 6 [1, 2, 3, 6]   (b) 16

Page 148   **Exercise 3M**

1. 3, 6, 9, 12   **2.** 4, 8, 12, 16   **3.** 2, 4, 6, 8   **4.** 7, 14, 21, 28

5. 10, 20, 30, 40   **6.** 5, 10, 15, 20, 25, 30   **7.** 8, 16, 24, 32, 40, 48   **8.** 9, 18, 27, 36, 45, 54

9. 11, 22, 33, 44, 55, 66   **10.** 20, 40, 60, 80, 100, 120   **11.** (a) 5   (b) 7

  (c) 2 and 4   **12.** 32   **13.** 101   **14.** 5

15. 56   **16.** 18   **17.** (a) 24, 60, 120 (b) 4, 6   **18.** (a) multiple

  (b) factor   (c) factor   (d) factor   **19.** 12, 24, 36

20. 10, 20, 30   **21.** 30, 60, 90   **22.** 12 and 24 or 48 and 96

Page 149   ***Exercise 3E***

1. (a) 2, 4, 6, 8, 10, 12   (b) 5, 10, 15, 20, 25, 30   (c) 10
2. (a) 4, 8, 12, 16   (b) 12, 24, 36, 48   (c) 12
3. (a) 3, 6, 9, 12, 15, 18   (b) 5, 10, 15, 20, 25, 30   (c) 15
4. (a) 18   (b) 24   (c) 70   (d) 12
   (e) 30   (f) 252   **5.** 12   **6.** 6
7. (a) 6   (b) 11   (c) 9   (d) 6
   (e) 12   (f) 10   **8.** (a) 6   (b) 40
   (c) 11, 22 (+ others)   (d) 2, 5   **9.** 15   **10.** 21

Page 150   ***Exercise 4M***

2. (a) 25   (b) 64   (c) 100   (d) 1   **3.** (a) 25
   (b) 14   (c) 181   **4.** (a) $4 + 9$ (b) $9 + 64$ (c) $4 + 36$
   (d) $81 + 100$ (e) $25 + 100$ (f) $16 + 81$ (g) $25 + 49$ (h) $49 + 64$
6. (a) 64   (b) 81   (c) 169
7. (b) $1 + 3 + 5 + 7 + 9 = 5^2$, $1 + 3 + 5 + 7 + 9 + 11 = 6^2$, $1 + 3 + 5 + 7 + 9 + 11 + 13 = 7^2$ etc

Page 151   ***Exercise 4E***

1. 8   **2.** (a) 7   (b) 11   (c) 13
3. (a) 2, 4, 8, 16   (b) 2, 3, 7   (c) 3, 9, 15, 21   (d) 4, 9, 16, 64
4. (a) $16 - 9$ (b) $81 - 1$ (c) $100 - 16$ (d) $400 - 100$
   (e) $49 - 4$ (f) $36 - 4$ (g) $64 - 25$ (h) $121 - 16$
5. (a) 5   (b) 9   (c) 7   (d) 1
6. (a) 7   (b) 14   (c) $\sqrt{441} = 21$ (d) $\sqrt{10.89} = 3.3$
7. (a) $1 + 9$ (b) $16 + 4 + 4$ (c) $36 + 9 + 1 + 1$ (d) $64 + 1 + 1$
   (e) $81 + 16 + 1$ (f) $49 + 9 + 4 + 1$ (g) $100 + 16 + 4$ (h) $121 + 16 + 4$
   (i) $225 + 196 + 1 + 1$ **8.** $4^3 = 64$, $5^3 = 125$, $6^3 = 216$ **9.** 8, 64, 1000
10. $13 + 15 + 17 + 19 = 64 = 4^3$ $21 + 23 + 25 + 27 + 29 = 125 = 5^3$
    $31 + 33 + 35 + 37 + 39 + 41 = 216 = 6^3$

Page 153   ***Satisfied numbers [Other solutions are possible]***

1.

	Number between 5 and 9	Square number	Prime number
Factor of 6	6	1	3
Even number	8	4	2
Odd number	7	9	5

2.

	Prime number	Multiple of 3	Factor of 16
Number greater than 5	7	9	8
Odd number	5	3	1
Even number	2	6	4

3. Many solutions.

Page 154   ***Happy numbers***

The Happy numbers are:- 1, 7, 10, 13, 19, 23, 28, 31, 32, 44, 49, 68, 70, 79, 82, 86, 91, 94, 97, 100
Encourage pupils to find 'short cuts'. E.g. if 23 is happy, so is 32.

Page 155   ***Check Yourself on Units 3.1, 3.2, 3.3, 3.4 and 3.5***

1. (b) 4   (d) parallelogram   **2.** (a) (5, 3)   (b) (7, 5)
   (c) (4, 3)   **3.** (a) 432   (b) 1944   (c) 144
4. (a) £39   (b) £24   **5.** (a) 2.0 cm   (b) 4.2 cm
   (c) 2.6 cm   (d) 0.7   (e) 0.03   (f) 0.15
6. (a) 0.08, 0.31, 0.411, 0.5   (b) 0.007, 0.1, 0.602, 0.62   (c) A = 0.27, B = 0.5
7. (a) 5.27   (b) 3.45   (c) 9.43   (d) £3.82
8. (a) 36.1   (b) 1.194   (c) 140   (d) 0.06
   (e) 1000   (f) 1000   (g) 10
9. (a) 13.5   (b) 3.84   (c) 12.32   (d) £6.10
10. (a) 4.71   (b) 5.3   (c) 5.5   (d) 0.32 kg
11. (a) 17   (b) 55   (c) 9   (d) 12 or 18
12. (a) 49   (b) 1   (c) 43   (d) 92
   (e) 36, 49   (f) 9, 25   (g) 1, 100

Page 159   ***Exercise 1M***

1. A: $y = 7$, B: $y = 3$, C: $y = 1\frac{1}{2}$ **2.** P: $x = 5$, Q: $x = 3$, R: $x = -3$
3. A: $x = 3$, B: $y = 2$, C: $y = -2$ **4.** A: $y = 2$, B: $x = 4$, C: $x = -2$
5. (a) (3, 2)   (b) (1, 5)   (c) (7, 3)   **6.** (a) $x = 1$ (b) $y = 7$
   (c) $x = 2$ (d) $x = 7$ (e) $x = 3$ (f) $y = 3$ (g) $y = 5$
   (h) $y = 0$

Page 161   ***Exercise 1E***

1. (1, 3), (2, 4), (3, 5) etc. $y = x + 2$ **2.** (1, 0), (2, 1), (3, 2) etc, $y = x - 1$
3. $y = x + 4$ **4.** $x + y = 6$ (or $y = 6 - x$)   **5.** $x + y = 4$ **6.** $y = 2x$
7. (a) $y = 2x + 1$ (b) $y = 2x - 4$ (c) $y = 11$ (d) $y = x - 5$ **8.** $y = \frac{1}{2}x + 8$
9. $y = 3x - 27$ **10.** $x + y = 7$ (or $y = 7 - x$)

Page 163   ***Exercise 2M***

1. (a) 7   (b) 9   (c) 4   **2.** (a) 3   (b) 5   (c) 7
3. (a) 6   (b) 15   (c) 0   **4.** A and C   **5.** B and C
6. A: $y = x + 2$, B: $y = 2x$, C: $y = 2x$, D: $y = 2x$, E: $y = x + 2$, F: $y = x + 2$
7. P, S and T are on $y = 3x - 2$; Q, R and U are on $y = x - 3$
8. $y = x - 2$: C; $y = 8 - x$; A; $x = 4$ not marked; $y = 4$: D; $y = 2x$: B

Page 164   **Exercise 2E**

1. (2, 5) (3, 6) (4, 7)
4. (2, –2) (3, –1) (4, 0)
7. (0, –2) (2, 2) (4, 6)
10. (0, 2) (1, 5) (2, 8)

2. (2, 7) (3, 8) (4, 9)
5. (2, 4) (3, 6) (4, 8)
8. (1, 5) (3, 3) (5, 1) (6, 0)
11. (2, 3)

3. (2, 0) (3, 1) (4, 2)
6. (0, 1) (2, 5) (4, 9)
9. (0, 4) (2, 2) (4, 0)

Page 166   **Exercise 1M**

1. (a) football   (b) 5   (c) 25   **2.** (a) 5   (b) 30
4. (a) 8   (b) £3.50   **5.** (a) 30 cm   (b) June   (c) December
    (d) April, May, July, September   (e) February, March, August, October

Page 167   **Exercise 1E**

1. (a) C   (b) D   (c) B   (d) A
2. (a) 40   (b) 10   (c) 40   (d) Belair
3. (a) 60% loss of farming land   (b) golf, walking, sports
    (c) loss of farming land used now for residential buildings
4. Wheat production has increased from 4 million tonnes to 14 million tonnes
    Rice production has not changed
    Sugar cane has increased to 2 million tonnes
    Cotton seed has increased to 3 million tonnes.
5. (a) Former commonwealth countries make up for the difference, plus U.S.A.
6. Tallies in order: E = 10, M = 10, F = 4, N = 15, S = 6

Page 170   **Exercise 2M**

1. (a) Frequencies: 1, 4, 3, 5, 7   (b) 12   **2.** (a) Frequencies: 2, 4, 8, 8
3. (a) 7   (b) 7   (c) 19   **4.** Pigs' weight has increased on high fibre diet

Page 172   **Exercise 2E**

1. Yes, there was some improvement in group X   **2.** 1992
3. (a) 30 litres   (b) 15.00   (c) 20 litres   (d) fuel tank was filled
    (e) car was stationary   (f) 60 litres
4. (a) warm and dry   (b) Wednesday   (c) Both days had little rain but higher temperature on Saturday

Page 174   **Exercise 3M**

1. (a) $\frac{1}{2}$ (b) $\frac{1}{4}$ (c) 100 g   **2.** (a) $\frac{1}{4}$ (b) $\frac{1}{8}$ (c) 10

3. 1208   **4.**

Method	car	walk	train	bus
Number of people	40	10	20	10

Page 175 **Exercise 3E**

1. (a) USA (b) Greece or USA (c) 25 **3.** (a) 50 (b) 75
4. (a) 8 boys chose red, 5 girls chose red, John is wrong (b) 10 boys chose blue, Tara is right

Page 178 **Exercise 1M and 1E**

For discussion.

Page 180 **Exercise 3M**

1. $\dfrac{3}{4}$ **2.** $\dfrac{1}{4}$ **3.** $\dfrac{1}{2}$ **4.** 0 **5.** $\dfrac{3}{5}$ **6.** $\dfrac{1}{3}$ **7.** 1

8. $\dfrac{11}{12}$ **9.** (a) $\dfrac{1}{2}$ (b) $\dfrac{1}{2}$ (c) $\dfrac{1}{6}$ (d) $\dfrac{1}{8}$ **11.** $\dfrac{1}{7}$

Page 182 **Exercise 3E**

1. (a) $\dfrac{1}{3}$ (b) $\dfrac{1}{3}$ (c) $\dfrac{1}{3}$ **2.** (a) $\dfrac{1}{4}$ (b) $\dfrac{1}{4}$ (c) $\dfrac{1}{4}$

3. (a) $\dfrac{1}{2}$ (b) $\dfrac{1}{2}$ (c) 0 **4.** (a) $\dfrac{2}{3}$ (b) $\dfrac{1}{3}$

5. (a) $\dfrac{6}{11}$ (b) $\dfrac{3}{11}$ (c) $\dfrac{1}{11}$ **6.** (a) $\dfrac{1}{6}$ (b) $\dfrac{1}{6}$ (c) $\dfrac{2}{3}$

7. (a) $\dfrac{1}{8}$ (b) $\dfrac{1}{2}$ (c) $\dfrac{5}{8}$ **8.** (a) $\dfrac{1}{9}$ (b) $\dfrac{1}{3}$ (c) $\dfrac{5}{9}$

9. (a) $\dfrac{7}{12}$ (b) $\dfrac{1}{6}$ (c) $\dfrac{5}{12}$ (d) $\dfrac{7}{12}$ **10.** (a) $\dfrac{4}{11}$ (b) $\dfrac{7}{11}$

11. (a) $\dfrac{2}{11}$ (b) $\dfrac{4}{11}$ (c) $\dfrac{5}{11}$ **12.** (a) $\dfrac{1}{8}$ (b) $\dfrac{1}{8}$ (c) $\dfrac{1}{4}$ (d) $\dfrac{1}{2}$

Page 184 **Check Yourself on Sections 3.6, 3.7 and 3.8**

1. (a) (1, 4) (b) $x = 1$ (c) $y = 2$ (d) (3, 3)
2. (a) $y = x - 2$ (b) $y = x + 3$ (c) $y = 2x$ (d) P and R
3. (a) (i) 18 (ii) £3.50 (iii) Prawn (b) (i) 10 (ii) 80
  (iii) You cannot have, for example, $2\frac{1}{2}$ bedrooms.
4. (a) Frequencies: 2, 3, 7, 14, 8, 3, 3
  (b) AB no rain and no use, BC it rains, CD no rain and no use, DE water used, EF no rain, FG it rains, GH no rain and no use.
5. (a) $\dfrac{1}{3}$ (b) 30 **7.** (a) $\dfrac{1}{4}$ (b) $\dfrac{5}{8}$ (c) $\dfrac{3}{8}$ (d) $\dfrac{1}{3}$

  (e) $\dfrac{1}{52}$ (f) $\dfrac{1}{13}$ (g) $\dfrac{1}{2}$ **8.** (a) (i) true (ii) true (iii) false

  (b) (i) white (ii) $\dfrac{7}{11}$ (iii) $\dfrac{3}{11}$ (iv) 0 (v) $\dfrac{1}{11}$

Page 187   **Exercise 1M**

1. £4.25   **2.** (a) 425   (b) 0   (c) 58   (d) 6823
   (e) 3035   (f) 65   (g) 120   (h) 340
3. (a) 246   (b) 1476   **5.** 127   **6.** 335   **7.** 12011
8. (a) 25 cm²   (b) 80 cm   **9.** 34 teams and 4 pupils left over
10. (a) 90 mm   (b) 9.0 cm

Page 189   **Exercise 2M**

1. (a) 17   (b) 12   (c) 48   (d) 200
2.

6	10	14	7
16	3	2	16
4	17	13	3
11	7	8	11

   3. 14   **4.** £300 000.00   **5.** (a) 2010 shekels
   (b) Rome   **6.** (a) 36   (b) 11, 17
   (c) 16, 36   **7.** (b) 80%   **8.** various answers
   9. (a) 12   (b) 4 cm   **10.** 63

Page 190   **Exercise 3M**

1. (a) 575 + 326 = 901   (b) 369 + 584 = 953   (c) 216 + 534 = 750
2. 10   **3.** (a) 23   (b) 3 – 7 – 15 – 31   (c) 6 – 13 – 27 – 55
4. 438   **5.** 5   **6.** 1600   **7.** 85   **8.** 47 days   **9.** 20
10. (a) 564   (b) 530   (c) 20   (d) 195   (e) 670   (f) 96

Page 191   **Exercise 4M**

1. £1928   **2.** 5 and 13   **3.** £24.50   **4.** 0.03, 0.2, 0.201, 0.32, 0.4
5. Just over 596 years   **6.** 6561   **7.** (a) 574 + 322 + 147 = 1043
   (b) 2324 + 3502 + 2315 = 8141   **8.** 0.72   **9.** 23

Page 192   **Exercise 5M**

1. (a) 1.3, 5.2, 52   (b) 0.35, 0.7, 70, 14   (c) 2.4, 24, 0.024, 0.048
2. (a) 2   (b) 20   (c) 1008 mm   **3.**
4. 440 g   **5.** 5 250 000   **6.** (a) 1014 mm
   (b) 101.4 cm   (c) more than 1 m
7. 54 × 3 = 162
9. (a) 1 – 2 – 5 – 14   **8.**
   (b) 4 – 11 – 32 – 95
   (c) 3 – 8 – 23 – 68
10. (a) 10 cm²   (b) 13 cm

×	3	7	8	4
5	15	35	40	20
6	18	42	48	24
9	27	63	72	36
2	6	14	16	8

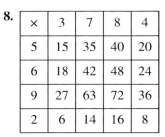

Page 193   Number rings

Multiples of 13 do not form number rings.
For example 13, 26, 39 etc.

Page 194   Unit 3 Mixed Review

1. (a) 7.1   (b) 100   (c) 10   (d) 1000   (e) 100   (f) 100

2. (a) What do you call a man with a spade in his head? Doug
    (b) Without, Douglas   (c) What do you call a dead parrot? Polygon

3. (a) x = 2   (b) y = 4   (c) y = x   **4.** (a) 4, 8, 12, 16, 20

    (b) 1, 2, 3, 4, 6, 12   (c) 2, 3   **5.** (a) $\frac{1}{6}$ (b) $\frac{5}{6}$ **6.** £27

7. (a) 3.27 + 1.74 = 5.01   (b) 4.55 + 0.63 = 5.18   (c) 3.64 − 1.57 = 2.07

8. (a) 0.605, 0.65, 0.7, 0.71   (b) 0.079, 0.08, 0.1, 0.99   (c) 1^3, (2×3), 2^3, 3^2

9. (a) 96   (b) 121   **10.** (a) 18   (b) 36   (c) 9

11. (2, 0), (3, 1), (4, 2)   **12.** (a) $\frac{1}{6}$ (b) $\frac{1}{8}$ (c) 1

13. (a) 55p   (b) £2.25   **14.** (a) $\frac{1}{2}$ (b) $\frac{1}{3}$ (c) $\frac{6}{7}$

15. (a) 11.3 − 12.8 − 128 − 125.1   (b) 0.06 × 100 − 6 − 5.8 − 0.58   (c) 255 − 2.55 − 3 − 3000

Page 196   Part two

1. (a) 16   (b) 20   (c) 44   **2.** (a) 231   (b) 225

3. 6110 seconds   **4.** (a) 4, 8, 12, 16, 20, 24, 28   (b) 7, 14, 21, 28, 35, 42   (c) 28

5. (a) stationary   (b) filled up with fuel   (c) half a tank   (d) 1800

6. €142.5   **7.** $8085   **8.** 0.1 mm   **9.** (From the top) 4, 8, 12, 12, 4

10. $\frac{1}{3}$ **11.** (a) 1.75   (b) 0.037   (c) 2.73   (d) 1.3

12. £8.30   **13.** 486   **14.** 504

15. (a) F   (b) T   (c) F   (d) F   (e) T

16. (a) £30   (b) £36   (c) 56 dollars   (d) 44 dollars   (e) £50

Page 200   Puzzles and Problems 3

1. (a) A = 4, B = 8, C = 11, D = 7   (b) A = 6, B = 2, C = 5, D = 4, E = 8
    (c) A = 6, B = 3, C = 1, D = 5   (d) A = 8, B = 3

2. (a)

(b)

(c)

(d)

(e)

(f)

3.
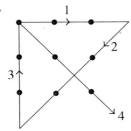

4. $\boxed{9} - \boxed{5} = \boxed{4}$
$\boxed{6} \div \boxed{3} = \boxed{2}$
$\boxed{1} + \boxed{7} = \boxed{8}$

5.
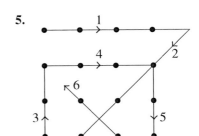

Page 202   ***A long time ago! 3***

Exercise

1. £7 9s. 4d.   **2.** £10 6s. 11d.   **3.** £13 11s. 2d.   **4.** £15 18s. 7d.   **5.** £21 8s. 2d.
6. £74 8s. 4d.   **7.** 48   **8.** 42   **9.** 5s. 6d.   **10.** 4d.   **11.** 6d.

Page 202   ***Mental Arithmetic Test 1***

1. £45   **2.** 350   **3.** 20%   **4.** £6.31   **5.** 40
6. 70°   **7.** 5: 35 pm   **8.** 100   **9.** 8.5   **10.** 24 cm²
11. south-west   **12.** 13   **13.** 5p, 5p, 5p, 5p, 1p   **14.** $\frac{1}{2}$ **15.** 8 cm
16. 45   **17.** 3600   **18.** false   **19.** £40 000   **20.** 11

Page 203   ***Mental Arithmetic   Test 2***

1. 56 m²   **2.** 700   **3.** 8   **4.** 3209   **5.** 36   **6.** 20
7. 9990   **8.** 5   **9.** 500 ± 50   **10.** $\frac{5}{6}$ **11.** 0.7   **12.** 1 million
13. 30   **14.** 0.47   **15.** isosceles   **16.** 8   **17.** 1000   **18.** 70%
19. 6   **20.** 4 h

Unit 4

Page 204   ***Exercise 1M***

1. (a) 48°　　(b) 115°　　(c) 33°　　**3.** (a) 40°　　(b) 110°　　(c) 55°
4. (a) 50°　　(b) 65°　　(c) 55°　　**5.** 9.4 cm

Page 205   ***Exercise 1E***

1. 7.0 cm　　**2.** 7.0 cm　　**3.** 7.4 cm　　**4.** 15.0 cm　　**5.** 9.4 cm　　**6.** 11.3 cm
7. m = 60°, n = 120°　　**8.** x = 115°, y = 65°

Page 207   ***Exercise 1E***

1. perpendicular **2.** LM perpendicular MN, ON parallel LM, OL parallel MN
3. CD perpendicular EF, AB parallel CD
4. CD and EF   **5.**　　　　　　　　　　**6.** (a) WZ　　(b) WX

8.

Page 210   ***Exercise 2M***

1. Scalene – B, E; isosceles – C, G, H, J; equilateral – F; right-angled – A, D, I
2. (a) trapezium　　　　(b) kite　　　　　　(c) regular hexagon　　(d) square
　　(e) rectangle　　　　(f) equilateral triangle　(g) heptagon　　　　(h) regular pentagon
　　(i) rhombus　　　　(j) regular decagon　　(k) trapezium　　　　(l) pentagon
　　(m) isosceles triangle　(n) quadrilateral　　(o) parallelogram　　(p) regular octagon
　　(q) hexagon　　　　(r) trapezium　　　　(s) rectangle　　　　(t) parallelogram

Page 211   ***Exercise 2E***

1. A–square, B–rhombus, C–kite, D–parallelogram, E–trapezium, F–rectangle
3. B　　　　　　**4.** diagonals are perpendicular, diagonals bisect each other
5. example:

Page 212   Investigation–Triangles and quadrilaterals

1. Eight different triangles:

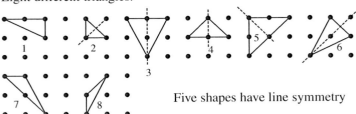

Five shapes have line symmetry

2. Sixteen diffe\rent quadrilaterals:

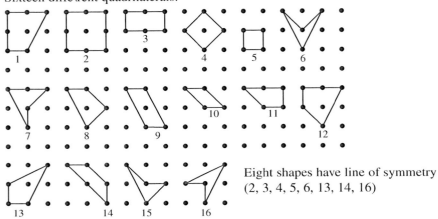

Eight shapes have line of symmetry
(2, 3, 4, 5, 6, 13, 14, 16)

*Page 213   **Check Yourself on Sections 4.1 and 4.2***

1. (a) 70°   (b) 5.3 cm or 5.4 cm **2.** (a) AB or CD
   (b) AB or CD   (c) AD or BC   (d) BC   **3.** (a) equilateral
   (b) scalene   (c) isosceles   (d) right-angled
   (e) two equal sides only and two equal angles only
4. (a) trapezium   (b) square   (c) rhombus   (d) kite   (e) parallelogram
   (f) four equal sides, opposite sides are parallel, opposite angles are equal
5. (a) P, R   (b) 10   (c) This shape is a regular octagon.

*Page 215   **Exercise 1M***

1. (a) $\frac{3}{5} = \frac{6}{10} = 0.6$ (b) $\frac{11}{20} = \frac{55}{100} = 0.55$

   (c) $0.9 = \frac{9}{10} = \frac{90}{100} = 90\%$ (d) $0.17 = \frac{17}{100} = 17\%$

2. $\frac{1}{20}$ **3.** (a) 0.37   (b) 0.6   (c) 0.06   (d) 0.19

(e) 0.45   **4.** (a) false   (b) true   (c) true   (d) false

(e) true   (f) false   **5.** (a) $\frac{4}{5}$ (b) $\frac{47}{100}$ (c) $\frac{4}{25}$

(d) $\frac{17}{20}$ (e) $\frac{3}{4}$

6.

$\frac{7}{10}$	0.7	70%
$\frac{6}{25}$	0.24	24%
$\frac{23}{50}$	0.46	46%
$\frac{19}{20}$	0.95	95%
$\frac{3}{20}$	0.15	15%

Page 216   Exercise 1E

1. (a) 0.34   (b) 0.76   (c) 0.65   (d) 0.45   **2.** (a) $\frac{7}{10}, \frac{3}{4}, 0.8$

(b) $\frac{11}{20}, 0.57, 60\%$ (c) $\frac{1}{5}, 24\%, \frac{1}{4}$ (d) 0.8, 82%, $\frac{21}{25}$

3. (a) $\frac{3}{4}$ (d) 75%   **4.** $\frac{64}{100}, \frac{128}{200}, \frac{16}{25}$ **5.** (a) $\frac{49}{100}$

(b) $\frac{2}{25}$ (c) $\frac{14}{25}$ (d) $\frac{3}{20}$

6. $\frac{17}{20}, 0.85, 85\%;$ $\frac{4}{5}, 0.8, 80\%;$ $\frac{1}{4}, 0.25, 25\%,$ $\frac{3}{25}, 0.12, 12\%;$ $\frac{22}{25}, 0.88, 88\%$

Page 217   Exercise 2M

1. (a) $\frac{1}{4}$ (b) 25%   **2.** (a) $\frac{3}{4}$ (b) 75%   **3.** (a) $\frac{3}{5}$ (b) 60%

4. (a) $\frac{1}{4}$ (b) 25%   **5.** (a) $\frac{2}{5}$ (b) 40%   **6.** (a) $\frac{2}{3}$ (b) $66\frac{2}{3}\%$

7. (a) $\frac{7}{10}$ (b) 70%   **8.** (a) $\frac{1}{3}$ (b) $33\frac{1}{3}\%$ **10.** (a) 60%   (b) 75%

(c) $33\frac{1}{3}\%$ (d) 50%   (e) 20%   **11.** $\frac{1}{5}$ **12.** $66\frac{2}{3}\%$ **13.** 70%

14. (a) 25%   (b) 75%   (c) 60%   (d) 20%   **15.** 10%

Page 219   Exercise 3M

1. (a) £15   (b) £18   (c) £7   (d) £14   (e) £27   (f) £20
2. 36   **3.** 20   **4.** 132   **5.** (a) £160   (b) £22   (c) £280
    (d) £12   (e) £4   (f) £12   **6.** 25% of £60   **7.** same   **8.** (b)
9. (a)   **10.** £3

Page 220   **Exercise 3E**

1. (a) £42	(b) £15	(c) £560	(d) £4	(e) £24	(f) £58 900
2. £3120	**3.** £8460	**4.** 3200	**5.** £46	**6.** 57 kg	**7.** 448
8. (a) £126	(b) £73.50	(c) £21	**9.** 475 g	**10.** £130	

Page 222   **Exercise 4M**

1. £26	**2.** (a) £3.75	(b) £3.70	(c) £0.49	(d) £1.80	
3. (a) £36.80	(b) £20.70	(c) £76.80	(d) £2774	(e) £96.90	(f) £1128
4. 324	**5.** 9% of £21	**6.** (a) 2190 kg	(b) 74.2 km	(c) $7.05	(d) 14.62 km
(e) 282 m	(f) 6958 g	**7.** 224			

Page 222   **Exercise 4E**

1. £239.20	**2.** (a) £213.90	(b) £697.50	(c) £437.10	(d) £799.80	**3.** 84.8 kg
4. (a) £81.20	(b) £186.20	(c) £201.60	(d) £4469	**5.** 2.94 kg	**6.** £182.40
7. 1.7874 kg	**8.** £362.10	**9.** £136 240			

Page 224   **Exercise 1M**

1. £100	**2.** £80	**3.** £12	**4.** 120 g	**5.** £1.71	**6.** £770
7. £75	**8.** £294	**9.** 3200	**10.** 18 litres	**11.** £750	**12.** £100
13. 10 minutes	**14.** £18	**15.** 10			

Page 225   **Exercise 1E**

1. $\frac{17}{40}$	**2.** (a) $\frac{1}{4}$	(b) $\frac{3}{8}$	**3.** $\frac{1}{4}$	**5.** 60%	**6.** 240 dollars
7. 153 euros	**8.** 192 dollars	**9.** 96 litres	**10.** 7840 yen		

Page 226   **Exercise 2M**

1. 5:2	**2.** 8:5	**3.** 1:2	**4.** 5:3	**5.** 11:16	**6.** 5:3
8. 19:14	**9.** 5:7	**10.** (a) 1:4	(b) 4:5	(c) 1:11	(d) 4:3
(e) 5:4:3	(f) 3:5	(g) 13:5	(h) 2:3:8	**12.** (a) 4	(b) 3
(c) 7	(d) 15	(e) 3	(f) 4		

Page 227   **Exercise 2E**

1. (a) £27:£9	(b) £6:£30	(c) £24:£12	**2.** (a) £10:£40	(b) £30:£20	(c) £15:£35
3. (a) £30:£45	(b) £33:£42	(c) £40:£35	**4.** (a) 16	(b) 12	**5.** 81
6. 18	**7.** Natasha £15: Andy £9	**8.** Mark 20:Helen 25	**9.** £10		
10. 12	**11.** 12 litres	**12.** £45			

Page 228 **Check Yourself on Sections 4.3 and 4.4**

1.

(a)	$\frac{2}{25}$	0.08	8%
(b)	$\frac{4}{5}$	0.8	80%
(c)	$\frac{9}{10}$	0.9	90%
(d)	$\frac{8}{25}$	0.32	32%
(e)	$\frac{18}{25}$	0.72	72%

2. (a) 75%   (b) 60%   (c) $33\frac{1}{3}$ %   **3.** (a) £18

(b) £285   (c) £96   **4.** (a) £56   (b) £2

5. (a) $\frac{1}{3}$ (b) $\frac{9}{22}$ **6.** (a) 2:3   (b) 3:8

(c) £35:£5   (d) 9

Page 230 **Exercise 1M**

1. (a) 4°C   (b) −7°C   (c) −3°C, −7°C, −2°C   **2.** −2, 3, −6, −12, −3
3. (a) 5°C   (b) −7°C   (c) −15°C   (d) 3 a.m.   (e) 20°C
4. (a) −5 < −4   (b) 0 > −2   (c) −3 > −6   **5.** (a) 6   (b) 5   (c) 7
(d) 7   (e) 12   (f) 8   **6.** (a) −9°C, −7°C, −4°C, −2°C, 5°C, 6°C
(b) −13°C, −5°C, −4°C, 4°C, 5°C, 23°C   (c) −7°C, −5°C, −2°C, 3°C, 5°C, 14°C
(d) −5°C, −3°C, −2°C, −1°C, 0°C, 5°C   **7.** −1°C   **8.** Test A:5, Test B:−1
9. −30 m   **10.** (a) eg. bottom of a lake   (b) floods, build dams

Page 233 **Exercise 1E**

1. (a) −8   (b) −20   (c) −12   (d) 6   (e) −18   (f) −16
(g) 30   (h) −7   **2.** (a) −4   (b) −5   (c) −4   (d) 3
(e) 3   (f) −5   (g) −5   (h) 3   **3.** (a) −2   (b) −48
(c) 28   (d) −32   (e) 2   (f) −3   (g) −90   (h) 9
4. −8, −1; −4, −2   **5.** (a)

×	−3	6	−1	4
5	−15	30	−5	20
−2	6	−12	2	−8
7	−21	42	−7	28
−5	15	−30	5	−20

(b)

×	−4	−7	2	0	−8	5
3	−12	−21	6	0	−24	15
−9	36	63	−18	0	72	−45
6	−24	−42	12	0	−48	30
−4	16	28	−8	0	32	−20
−6	24	42	−12	0	48	−30
−1	4	7	−2	0	8	−5

6. (a) −8   (b) 30   (c) 9   (d) 36   (e) −32   (f) −40
(g) 100   (h) 1   **7.** (a) 7   (b) −7   (c) −2   (d) −9
(e) −50   (f) 72

Page 234   **Exercise 2M**

1. (a) −2	(b) −5		**2.** (a) −3	(b) 2	(c) −4	(d) 3		
(e) −3	(f) −6		(g) −6	(h) −1	(i) −8	(j) 6		
(k) 0	(l) −4		**3.** (a) −6	(b) −6	(c) −8	(d) −13		
(e) 2	(f) 4		(g) −11	(h) −4	(i) 0	(j) −9		
(k) −7	(l) −12		**4.** (a) 9	(b) 0	(c) −7	(d) −9		
(e) 0	(f) −12		(g) 1	(h) −2	(i) −30	(j) −20		
(k) −40	(l) −4		**5.** −8					

Page 236   **Exercise 2E**

1. (a) 4	(b) 11	(c) −5	(d) −3	(e) −9	(f) −11
(g) −2	(h) 10	(i) 16	(j) −12	(k) 0	(l) −11
2. (a) 1	(b) −6	(c) 1	(d) 0	(e) −4	(f) −3
(g) −1	(h) 0	(i) −12	(j) −7	(k) 1	(l) −7
3. (a) 4	(b) 10	(c) −2	(d) −4	(e) −2	(f) −9

4. (a)
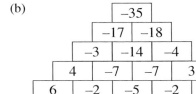
(b)

5. (a) true   (b) false   (c) true   (d) true   (e) false   (f) false
      (g) true   (h) false   (i) false

6. DYNAMIC

Page 237   **Exercise 1M**

1. y = 19	**2.** m = 40	**3.** w = 5	**4.** a = 8	**5.** c = 72
6. y = 49	**7.** p = 47	**8.** f = 72	**9.** m = 12	**10.** a = 80
11. p = 162	**12.** s = 8	**13.** c = 245	**14.** v = 34	

Page 238   **Exercise 1E**

1. (a) x = −3	(b) y = −13	**2.** a = 2	**3.** w = 19	**4.** m = −27
5. h = −24	**6.** c = −15	**7.** n = −10	**8.** p = 36	**9.** a = −9
10. y = 30	**11.** p = −10	**12.** a = −18	**13.** c = 12	**14.** y = −21
15. p = −6				

Page 240   **Exercise 2M**

1. 8	**2.** 12	**3.** 20	**4.** 6	**5.** 9	**6.** 7
7. 5	**8.** 8	**9.** 6	**10.** 4	**11.** 9	**12.** 8

Page 241   **Exercise 3M**

1. 7	**2.** 13	**3.** 12	**4.** 17	**5.** 8	**6.** 10

7. 2	**8.** 8	**9.** 8	**10.** 0	**11.** 24	**12.** 12
13. 3	**14.** 3	**15.** 9	**16.** 5	**17.** 1	**18.** $\frac{1}{2}$
19. 25	**20.** 0	**21.** 6	**22.** 20	**23.** 10	**24.** 500
25. 24	**26.** 4	**27.** 20	**28.** 38	**29.** 8	**30.** 51
31. 0	**32.** 7	**33.** 3	**34.** 84	**35.** 1	**36.** $\frac{1}{3}$
37. 90	**38.** 160	**39.** 103	**40.** 315	**41.** 27	**42.** 500
43. 0	**44.** 0	**45.** 60			

Page 242   **Exercise 3E**

1. 3	**2.** 7	**3.** 4	**4.** 2	**5.** 5	**6.** 9
7. 10	**8.** 1	**9.** 3	**10.** 5	**11.** 20	**12.** 6
13. 4	**14.** 8	**15.** 10	**16.** 7	**17.** 7	**18.** 0
19. 5	**20.** 4	**21.** 20	**22.** 50	**23.** 6	**24.** $\frac{1}{2}$

Page 243   **Exercise 4M**

1. 2	**2.** 8	**3.** 3	**4.** 10	**5.** 7	**6.** 5
7. 30	**8.** 8	**9.** 5	**10.** 7	**11.** (a) 45	(b) 30
12. 27					

Page 244   **Exercise 4E**

1. 9	**2.** 6	**3.** 1	**4.** 12	**5.** 3	**6.** 5
7. 0	**8.** 15	**9.** 14	**10.** 9	**11.** 6	**12.** 1
13. 25	**14.** 9	**15.** 45	**16.** 11	**17.** 9	**18.** 22
19. 110	**20.** 65	**21.** 201			

Page 245   **Exercise 5M**

1. $2x + 6$	**2.** $6x + 24$	**3.** $3x + 27$	**4.** $5x + 40$	**5.** $4x - 28$
6. $2x - 16$	**7.** $9x - 36$	**8.** $6x - 48$	**9.** $4x + 4y$	**10.** $7a + 7b$
11. $3m - 3n$	**12.** $10x + 15$	**13.** $24x - 42$	**14.** $8a + 4b$	**15.** $9m + 18n$
16. $4x + 12y$	**17.** $8m + 2n$	**18.** $35x - 21$	**19.** $24 - 8x$	**20.** $24 - 12x$
21. $15a + 25b$	**22.** $18m + 9$	**23.** $22t - 33$	**24.** $4a - 8c$	**25.** $3x + 3y + 3z$
26. $5a + 10b + 5c$	**27.** $14x + 7y + 21$	**28.** $12x - 20$	**29.** $48 - 6x$	**30.** $8x + 16y - 8$

Page 246   **Exercise 5E**

1. $pq + pr$	**2.** $mn - mp$	**3.** $ab + ac$	**4.** $ab - ae$	**5.** $xy + 3x$
6. $mn - 6m$	**7.** $xy - 9x$	**8.** $pq - 5p$	**9.** $ac + 7a$	**10.** $de + 8d$
11. $a^2 + 4a$	**12.** $m^2 - 6m$	**13.** $p^2 - 2p$	**14.** $x^2 + 9x$	**15.** $7a - a^2$
16. $2x + xy$	**17.** $10a + 15$	**18.** $27m - 18$	**19.** $24x - 6$	**20.** $32n + 28$
21. $4b - b^2$				

Page 246   ***Check Yourself on Sections 4.5 and 4.6***

1. (a) 2°C, 1°C, –3°C, –4°C, –8°C, –9°C,   (b) –5   **2.** (a) –15   (b) 8
(c) –3   (d) 32   **3.** (a) –4   (b) –7   (c) –3
(d) –2   **4.** (a) 28   (b) 4   **5.** (a) 26   (b) 30
(c) 10   (d) 7   **6.** (a) $5x + 35$ (b) $np – 3n$ (c) $x^2 + 8x$

Page 247   ***Mixed Review*** **Part one**

1. £42   **2.** £27   **3.** parallelogram   **4.** –4°C   **5.** (a) 6

(b) 5   (c) 56   **6.** £3.60   **7.** 24%   **8.** $\dfrac{7}{10}$

9. 540 litres   **10.** £360   **11.** 5.7 cm   **12.** (a) $\dfrac{3}{4}$ (b) $\dfrac{6}{7}$

(c) $\dfrac{23}{25}$ (d) $\dfrac{3}{5}$ **13.** (a) 3, 6   (b) –8, – 3   (c) –8, – 3, 0, 3, 6

(d) 14   **14.** (a) $5x – 15$ (b) $6x + 12$ **15.** 3:5

Page 248   ***Part two***

1. (a) 6°C   (b) –3°C   **2.** 16   **4.** $\dfrac{7}{25}$ **5.** (a) 24   (b) 9   (c) 22

6. 6   **7.** £2500   **8.** $n(n + 4) = n^2 + 4n$ **9.** $x = 20°, 50°, 40°, 90°$

10. (a) 1:4   (b) 20%   **11.** 17   **13.** £44.55

Page 252   ***A long time ago! 4***

1. (a) 7   (b) 13   (c) 16   (d) 27   (e) 18   (f) 19
(g) 45   (h) 72   (i) 327   (j) 94   (k) 2006   (l) 949
2. (a) VIII   (b) XVII   (c) XXII   (d) LVIII   (e) XXXIX
(f) LXXXIV   (g) LXXVIII   (h) CXXIII   (i) CCCXXXIX   (j) MCCLXV
(k) MLXVI   (l) MMMCXCIV
4. (a) IX   (b) XVII   (c) XXX   (d) XXXIV   (e) XXXV
(f) LIII   (g) CCCXI   (h) X   (i) XXXVI   (j) CXXXIII
(k) XLII   (l) LXXXIV   (m) VIII   (n) V   (o) VI
(p) IV   (q) XL   (r) MCCCXXXIX

Page 254   ***Mental Arithmetic Test 1***

1. 20   **2.** 15   **3.** 36m   **4.** North-east   **5.** 94%   **6.** $\dfrac{7}{10}$
7. 8:15 pm   **8.** 6204   **9.** 69   **10.** 9   **11.** 31   **12.** 7:50
13. 3p   **14.** 53   **15.** 9   **16.** 80%   **17.** 400
18. 10p, 10p, 10p, 10p or 20p, 10p, 5p, 5p   **19.** 30°   **20.** 60

Page 254   ***Test 2***

1. 5   **2.** 10%   **3.** £6.01   **4.** 240   **5.** 45   **6.** 2015   **7.** 22
8. 92   **9.** 9   **10.** £10.50   **11.** £25   **12.** 8   **13.** 3.5   **14.** 4500
15. 20   **16.** 65°   **17.** 1200   **18.** north   **19.** 30°   **20.** £40.11

Unit 5

Page 256   ***Exercise 1M***

1. (a) 90° CW   (b) 180°   (c) 90° ACW   (d) 90° ACW   (e) 90° CW

(f) 180°   **11.** 90° CW   **12.** 90°ACW   **13.** 180°   **14.** 90° ACW

15. 180°   **16.** 90° ACW

Page 258   ***Exercise 1E***

5. (a) U   (b) T   (c) R   (d) T   (e) T

Page 259   ***Exercise 2M***

1. 3   **2.** No   **3.** 2   **4.** No   **5.** No   **6.** 2

7. 4   **8.** 2   **9.** 5   **10.** 8   **11.** 5   **12.** No

13. 6   **14.** 6   **15.** 3   **16.** 4

Page 260   ***Exercise 2E***

1. (a) yes   (b) 4

2.

3.
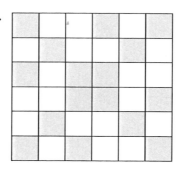

4.
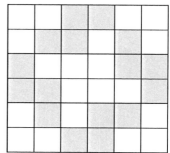

5.
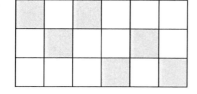

6.
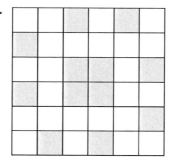

7.
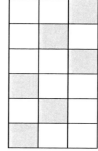

Page 262   ***Exercise 1M***

1. One line   **2.** One line   **3.** Four lines   **4.** Four lines   **5.** One line   **6.** Four lines

Page 262 **Exercise 1E**

2. (a) E, H, T   (b) N, Z, H   (c) H   **3.** A, B, C, D, E, H, I, K, M, O, T, U, V, W, X, Y
4. (a) No   (b) Yes   5, 6, 7   Own designs

Page 263 **Exercise 2M**

1. 3   **2.** 4   **3.** 5   **4.** 9   **5.** 9   **6.** 10

Page 264 **Exercise 2E**

1. 2   **2.** 3   **3.** 3   **4.** 6   **5.** 28   **6.** 17

Page 264 **Exercise 3M**

1. 19 possible designs

Page 267 **Exercise 1M**

2. (a) 2 right, 3 down   (b) 5 right, 3 up   (c) 4 left, 1 up   (d) 7 left
3. (e) 2 right, 4 down

Page 267 **Exercise 1E**

1. (a) E   (b) C   (c) F   (d) E
2. 1 right, 2 up;   5 right;   3 down;   2 left;   2 up;   2 left;   1 left, 2 down;   1 left, 1 up.
3. (a) 2 units right   (b) BC
    (c) 90°Clockwise about B, 90°anticlockwise about C, 180° about mid-point of BC

Page 268 **Check Yourself on Units 5.1, 5.2 and 5.3**

2. (a) 2   (b) 6   (c) 3   (d) 2   (e)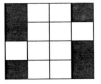
3.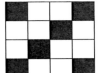

5. (b) (i) 3 units right and 2 units up   (ii) 2 units left and 1 unit up   (iii) 4 units up

Page 270 **Exercise 1M**

1. 16, 20, 24, 28   **2.** (a) 3, 6, 9, 12, 15   (b) 7, 14, 21, 28, 35   (c) 2, 4, 6, 8, 10
    (d) 10, 20, 30, 40, 50   **3.** (a) 83   (b) 18   (c) 69
4. (a) 3   (b) 15   (c) 9, 18   **5.** (a) 48   (b) 20   (c) 111
    (d) 1   **6.** 2, 3, 5, 7, 11, 13, 17, 19   **7.** 11, 31, 71   **8.** Many answers e.g. 2 + 3 = 5

Page 271 **Exercise 1E**

1. 87 squares are shaded   **2.** 4, 9   **3.** 2   **4.** (a) 1, 2, 5   (b) 20, 30
5. 6, 12, 18 etc   **6.** 15, 30, 45 etc   **7.** (b) 1, 11   (c) 14, 35   (d) 6, 9, 12
    (e) 3, 15, 13   (f) 2, 4   **8.** (a) 4, 8, 12, 16, 20, 24
    (b) 5, 10, 15, 20, 25, 30   (c) 20   **9.** (a) 3, 6, 9, 12, 15, 18, 21
    (b) 7, 14, 21, 28, 35, 42, 49   (c) 21   **10.** 15   **11.** 6   **12.** (a) 3
    (b) 12   (c) 4

Page 273 **Exercise 2M**

1. (a) 9   (b) 20   (c) 3   (d) 12   (e) 24
    (f) 15   (g) 18   (h) 15

2. (a) $\frac{4}{5}$ (b) $\frac{3}{4}$ (c) $\frac{3}{5}$ (d) $\frac{1}{4}$ (e) $\frac{7}{9}$
    (f) $\frac{9}{10}$ (g) $\frac{3}{7}$ (h) $\frac{7}{8}$ (i) $\frac{3}{7}$ (j) $\frac{1}{4}$

3. (a) $\frac{3}{5}$ (b) $\frac{5}{7}$ (c) $\frac{1}{3}$ (d) $\frac{7}{8}$ (e) $\frac{13}{20}$
    (f) $\frac{7}{10}$ (g) $\frac{1}{3}$ (h) $\frac{19}{35}$

4. (a) 0.3   (b) 0.25   (c) 0.6   (d) 0.75   (e) 0.09
    (f) 0.27   (g) 0.5   (h) 0.25   (i) 0.12   (j) 0.16

5. (a) 20%   (b) 15%   (c) 4%   (d) 45%   (e) 22%   (f) 44%

Page 274 **Exercise 2E**

1. (a) $\frac{1}{5}$ (b) $\frac{9}{10}$ (c) $\frac{3}{100}$ (d) $\frac{11}{100}$ (e) $\frac{43}{100}$
    (f) $\frac{3}{100}$ (g) $\frac{3}{20}$ (h) $\frac{17}{20}$ (i) $\frac{6}{25}$ (j) $\frac{1}{20}$

2. (a) $\frac{3}{10}$ (b) $\frac{3}{4}$ (c) $\frac{3}{25}$ (d) $\frac{7}{20}$ (e) $\frac{1}{25}$

3. Isabel 70%, Dani 60%   **4.** (a) $33\frac{1}{3}$%   (b) 40%   (c) 75%

    (d) 3%   (e) $66\frac{2}{3}$%   (f) 0.1%   **5.** (a) 0.42   (b) 0.67

    (c) 0.09   (d) 0.07   (e) 0.94   **6.** (a) $\frac{2}{5}$, 0.4, 40%   (b) $\frac{3}{20}$, 0.15, 15%

    (c) $\frac{3}{25}$, 0.12, 12%   (d) $\frac{4}{25}$, 0.16, 16%   (e) $\frac{1}{25}$, 0.04, 4%   **7.** (a) 60%, 0.7, $\frac{3}{4}$

    (b) $\frac{1}{50}$, 0.03, 5%   (c) 23%, 0.3, $\frac{3}{9}$ **8.** (a) 20%   (b) $\frac{11}{20}$ (c) 8%   (d) $\frac{6}{25}$

Page 274 **Exercise 3M**

1. 322   **2.** 595   **3.** 621   **4.** 1248   **5.** 1960   **6.** 2952

7. 2375   **8.** 7704   **9.** (a) 375   (b) 561   (c) 1134

10. (a) 56   (b) 17   (c) 26   (d) 45

Page 275   ***Exercise 3E***

1. 5   **2.** 805   **3.** 1   **4.** 3388 g   **5.** 36

Page 275   ***Exercise 4M***

1. (a) 9.2   (b) 24.8   (c) 2.54   (d) 4.14   (e) 1.538
    (f) 7.8   (g) 17.6   (h) 13.7

2. (a) 6.54 + 1.73 = 8.27   (b) 4.75 + 4.35 = 9.10   (c) 6.872 + 1.219 = 8.091

3. £18.24   **4.** 0.021   **5.** £1, 50p, 20p, 5p, 2p

6. (a) 6.89–1.32 = 5.57   **7.**
    (b) 8.73–3.26 = 5.47
    (c) 7.48–6.78 = 0.70

Page 276   ***Exercise 4E***

1. (a) 32.6   (b) 114   (c) 41.5   (d) 120   (e) 1.76   (f) 4.27
    (g) 1.653   (h) 0.042   **2.** false   **3.** (a) 10   (b) 1.7   (c) 1.6
    (d) 0.854   (e) 1   (f) 0.02   **4.** £12   **5.** 57.4 g

6. (a) 2.4 → 24 → 0.24 → 2.4   (b) 0.43 → 43 → 0.043 → 4.3   (c) 1.4 → 7 → 21 → 2.1

7. 16   **8.** 2.4   **9.** (a) 32.92   (b) 0.78   (c) 1.24   (d) 3.4
    (e) 5.3   (f) 8.61   (g) 1.42   (h) 48.12   **10.** £8.40

Page 277   ***Exercise 5M***

1. (a) 23   (b) 46   (c) 16   (d) 48   (e) 16   (f) 64
    (g) 75   (h) 225

2. (a) $\frac{1}{7}$ (b) $\frac{1}{11}$ (c) $\frac{1}{2}$ (d) 18   (e) $\frac{2}{3}$ (f) $\frac{1}{100}$

3. 9   **4.** 240   **5.** (a) £80   (b) £15   (c) £11   (d) 2 kg
    (e) 300   (f) 30   (g) 18 g   (h) 21 cm

6. (a) T   (b) T   (c) F   (d) T   (e) F   (f) T

Page 278   ***Exercise 5E***

1. All except $\frac{3}{5}$ **2.** (a) 25%   (b) 40%   (c) $33\frac{1}{3}\%$ (d) 2%

3. (a) £7.50   (b) 28 km   (c) £137   (d) £9900   (e) 192 kg

    (f) 220 miles   **4.** 900   **5.** (a) 0.15, 20%, $\frac{1}{4}$ (b) 0.05, 52%, $\frac{3}{5}$

    (c) 66%, $\frac{2}{3}$, 0.7   **6.** 18% of 300   **7.** 70.4   **8.** £141.50

Book 7C

47

Page 279   **Exercise 1M**

1. $\frac{1}{2}$ **2.** (a) $\frac{1}{4}$ (b) $\frac{1}{8}$ (c) $\frac{1}{3}$ (d) $\frac{1}{2}$

3. (a) $\frac{3}{5}$ (b) $\frac{2}{5}$ **4.** (a) $\frac{1}{3}$ (b) $\frac{1}{3}$ **5.** (a) $\frac{1}{7}$ (b) $\frac{2}{7}$

6. Bag A   **7.** (a) $\frac{1}{9}$ (b) $\frac{4}{9}$ (c) $\frac{4}{9}$

Page 280   **Exercise 1E**

1. (a) $\frac{1}{5}$ (b) $\frac{2}{5}$ **2.** (a) $\frac{1}{6}$ (b) $\frac{1}{2}$ (c) 0

3. (a) $\frac{1}{2}$ (b) $\frac{2}{5}$ **4.** (a) $\frac{1}{6}$ (b) $\frac{1}{3}$

5. (a) $\frac{1}{5}$ (b) 0   (c) $\frac{2}{5}$ **6.** $\frac{1}{150}$

7. (a) 1   (b) 0   **8.** $\frac{1}{55}$

Page 282   **Exercise 2M**

1. (a) $\frac{1}{13}$ (b) $\frac{1}{52}$ (c) $\frac{1}{4}$ **2.** (a) $\frac{1}{4}$ (b) $\frac{1}{2}$ (c) $\frac{1}{13}$

   (d) $\frac{3}{13}$ (e) $\frac{1}{52}$ **3.** (a) $\frac{1}{20}$ (b) $\frac{1}{5}$ (c) $\frac{1}{5}$ (d) $\frac{1}{2}$

   (e) $\frac{1}{4}$ **4.** (a) $\frac{5}{8}$ (b) $\frac{3}{8}$ (c) $\frac{1}{8}$ **5.** (a) $\frac{3}{11}$ (b) $\frac{5}{11}$

   (c) $\frac{1}{11}$ **6.** (a) $\frac{5}{9}$ (b) $\frac{1}{3}$ (c) $\frac{1}{9}$ (d) $\frac{5}{11}$ **7.** $\frac{2}{3}$

8. (a) (i) $\frac{2}{11}$ (ii) $\frac{3}{11}$ (b) (i) $\frac{5}{11}$ (ii) $\frac{2}{11}$

9. (a) True; she has a $\frac{1}{6}$ chance, Ben as $\frac{1}{7}$ (b) False; chance for Sarah is $\frac{1}{2}$, but Ben's is $\frac{3}{7}$

   (c) False

Page 283   **Exercise 2E**

1. 1 red ball and 1 white ball   **2.** 2 white balls and 1 red ball

3. 2 red balls and 1 white ball   **4.** 1 red ball and 3 white balls

5. 6 black balls and 3 white balls   **6.** (a) $\frac{1}{9}$ (b) $\frac{2}{3}$

7. (a) $\frac{1}{8}$ (b) $\frac{1}{2}$ (c) 1   **8.** (a) $\frac{5}{7}$ (b) 0   (c) $\frac{4}{7}$

9. (a) ABC, ACB, BAC, BCA, CAB, CBA   (b) $\frac{1}{3}$ (c) $\frac{2}{3}$ (d) $\frac{2}{3}$

10. Alan did the experiment properly

Page 285   **Exercise 1M**

1. (a) 32 km   (b) 40 miles   (c) 16 km   (2) (a) (i) £3.60   (ii) £1.40   (iii) £3.20

   (iv) £4.60   (b) (i) 390   (ii) 190   (iii) 330   (iv) 70   (c) £3.80

3. (a) (i) 37°   (ii) 39°   (b) 10.00   (v) 9.00 and 11.00   (d) 8.30 – 9.00

4. (a) 1400 m   (b) 1600 m   (c) 1200 m   (d) 11.00 and 13.00   (e) 2400 m
(f) 30 minutes   (g) 3 h

Page 287   **Exercise 1E**

1. (a) (i) £200   (ii) £600   (iii) £400   (b) £200   **2.** (a) 50p
(b) 30 seconds   (c) 75 seconds   **3.** (a) 30 litres   (b) 15.00   (c) 20 litres
(d) tank filled   (e) engine off   (f) 60 litres

Page 288   **Exercise 2M**

1. (a) about 2.6 pounds   (b) about 0.9 kg   **2.** (a) 25°C   (b) 59°F   **3.** (b) £23

Page 289   **Exercise 2E**

1. (a) 100 km   (b) 1h   (c) 08.15   (d) (i) 60 km/h   (ii) 80 km/h
2. (a) 40 km   (b) 09.15   (c) (i) 100 km/h   (ii) 40 km/h   (d) $2\frac{1}{2}$ hours

3. (a) $\frac{1}{2}$ hour   (b) 17.00   (c) 15.15   (d) (i) 20 km/h   (ii) 100 km/h

Page 290   **Test Yourself Units 5.5 and 5.6**

1. (a) (i) $\frac{3}{7}$ (ii) $\frac{2}{7}$ (b) $\frac{3}{7}$ **2.** (a) 15°C   (b) October
(c) April and November   (d) April, May   (e) 21°C   **3.** (a) 37.5 miles   (b) 32 km

Page 291   **Exercise 1M**

1. 8x + 2y   **2.** 4a + c   **3.** 3m + 3n   **4.** 9h + 4x   **5.** 5e   **6.** 9b
7. (a) T   (b) F   (c) T   (d) T   (e) F   (f) T
8. (a) a   (b) a^2 (c) m   (d) 5ab   (e) 4a
9. 9   **10.** 25   **11.** 17   **12.** 10   **13.** 10   **14.** 45
15. 34   **16.** 2   **17.** 24   **18.** 0   **19.** 1   **20.** 4
21. $m + m + m = 3m$, $m \times m = m^2$, $m \div 2 = \dfrac{m}{2}$

Page 292   **Exercise 1E**

1. 14   **2.** −1   **3.** 73   **4.** 12   **5.** 0   **6.** −15
7. 8   **8.** 35   **9.** (a) F   (b) T   (c) T   (d) T
(e) F   (f) T   **10.** 4 999 998

Page 294   **Exercise 1M**

1. (a) 8   (b) 10   (c) 11   (d) 9   (e) 12
(f) 57   (g) 21   (h) 108   (i) 1   (j) 17
2. (a) T   (b) T   (c) T   (d) F   (e) T
(f) F   (g) T   (h) T

3. (a) 70   (b) 90   (c) 20   (d) 40   (e) 80
(f) 130   (g) 250   (h) 20   (i) 30   (j) 190

4. (a) 1680   (b) 1720   (c) 1690   (d) 1700   (e) 1720

5. (a) 600   (b) 300   (c) 600   (d) 900   (e) 700
(f) 300   (g) 700   (h) 200   (i) 1500   (j) 28 400

6. (a) 5000   (b) 1000   (c) 1000   (d) 2000   (e) 7000
(f) 1000   (g) 3000   (h) 26 000   (i) 14 000   (j) 295 000

Page 294   **Exercise 1E**

1. (a) (i) 8   (ii) 27   (iii) 10   (b) (i) 90   (ii) 310   (iii) 5270
(c) (i) 700   (ii) 5300   (iii) 12 700

2. (a) ten   (b) whole number   (c) hundred   (d) ten   (e) thousand
(f) whole number

3. (a) 56800   (b) 2000   (c) 100   (d) 7200   (e) 900   (f) 9400
(g) 300   (h) 100   (i) 800

4. (a) 34   (b) 81   (c) 216   (d) 59   (e) 40   (f) 23
(g) 122   (h) 12   (i) 23   (j) 156   (k) 6   (l) 21

5. (a) 163 cm   (b) 160 cm   (c) 2 m

Page 296   **Exercise 2M**

1. (a) 2.4   (b) 8.9   (c) 4.7   (d) 12.5   (e) 16.4

2. (a) 1.9   (b) 4.1   (c) 10.0   (d) 65.4   (e) 14.0

3. (a) 18.8   (b) 3.6   (c) 17.1   (d) 0.8   (e) 5.4   (f) 11.3
(g) 10.3   (h) 7.1   **4.** (a) 4   (b) 12   (c) 0   (d) 138
(e) 11   (f) 7   (g) 7   (h) 5   **5.** (a) 9.3   (b) 59.5
(c) 0.8   (d) 129.8   (e) 1.4   (f) 11.7   (g) 22.6   (h) 27.3

Page 296   **Exercise 2E**

1. (a) (i) 8   (ii) 1   (iii) 8   (iv) 5   (b) (i) 8.4
(ii) 0.8   (iii) 7.9   (iv) 5.0

2. (a) 1.6   (b) 19.4   (c) 0.2   (d) 2.2   (e) 1.2
(f) 4.6   (g) 74.6   (h) 7.9

3. (Teacher's note: Many 'ordinary' rulers are not very accurate! If necessary, allow for minor differences to the following answers.)
(a) 8.2 cm   (b) 2.2 cm   (c) 10.9 cm   (d) 5.5 cm   (e) 12.8 cm

4. (a) (i) 5.0×3.6 (ii) 6.1×3.9 (b) (i) 18.0 cm^2 (ii) 23.8 cm^2

Page 298   **Exercise 3M**

1. 1000   **2.** 70   **3.** 60   **4.** 200   **5.** 400   **6.** 30
7. 8000   **8.** 10 000   **9.** 30   **10.** 800 000   **11.** 150   **12.** 80
13. 60   **14.** 20   **15.** 1   **16.** 300   **17.** 0.6   **18.** 8000
19. £4000   **20.** £20

Page 298   **Exercise 3E**

1. (a) £24   (b) £23.88   **2.** £80   **3.** (a) 120 cm²   (b) 118.34 cm²
4. £150   **5.** £4800   **6.** £300   **7.** (a) 48.99   (b) 1.96
  (c) 214.2   (d) 15.33   (e) 103.8   (f) 7.657   **8.** (a) 20.64
  (b) 52.56   (c) 200.9   (d) 1.19   (e) 9.13   (f) 0.14

Page 299   **Test Yourself on Units 5.7 and 5.8**

1. (a) $4a + 7c$ (b) $2ab$ (c) $8m + 2n$ (d) x (e) $2c$
  (f) $6a + ab$ (g) 9   (h) 28   **2.** (a) (i) 560   (ii) 2050
  (iii) 70   (b) (i) 5.7   (ii) 9.2   (iii) 0.8   (iv) 5.4
3. (a) 150   (b) 40   (c) 10   (d) £60

Page 300   **Mixed Review**   **Part one**

1. £8.33   **2.** 18   **3.** $\frac{4}{7}$ **4.** (a) $7n + 2$ (b) $4m + 9n$
  (c) $7c + 5$ (d) $20n + 16$ **5.** 6065   **6.** £36
7. (a) 30   (b) 19   (c) 25   (d) 10 is a factor of 30
8. 3   **9.** (4, 5)   **10.** £5.40 and £8.10   **11.** (a) 20°C   (b) 16°C
  (c) 17.00 and 22.30   (d) 15.00   (e) 22.00   **12.** 105 beats per minute
13. (a) 5.35 + 3.74 = 9.09   (b) 7.98 − 3.83 = 4.15   (c) 43.7 + 26.3 = 70.0
14. (b) right-angled vertex $\rightarrow (1, -1)$ (c) right-angled vertex $\rightarrow (6, 0)$

Part two

1. (a) £6.30   (b) £3.33   (c) £11.25   (d) £0.54   **2.** (a) 4   (b) 2
  (c) 2, 3, 11   (d) 15   (e) 2, 3, 8   (f) 9   **3.** 184 cm   **4.** (a) $\frac{1}{10}$
  (b) $\frac{1}{12}$ (c) $\frac{1}{20}$ **5.** (a) 96 cm²   (b) 48 cm   (c) Rotational symmetry of order 4
6. (a) 5 + 4 − 2 = 7 or 5 + 3 − 1 = 7   (b) (5 + 4) ÷ 3 = 3   (c) (4 + 2) ÷ (5 − 1) = $1\frac{1}{2}$
  (d) (5 + 4 + 2) × 3 = 33   **7.** 320 seconds (or 5 min 20 sec)
8. $\frac{7}{8}$ is closer (differences are $\frac{1}{8}$ and $\frac{1}{7}$)   **9.** £33.46   **10.** (a) 5.5   (b) 0.3
  (c) 2.2   **11.** (a) $\frac{2}{6}$ (b) $\frac{2}{87}$ **12.** many answers, e.g. 28 + 15 − 13 = 30
14. (a) $\frac{3}{4}$ (b) $\frac{4}{5}$ (c) $\frac{24}{25}$ (d) $\frac{2}{3}$

Page 305 **Puzzles and problems 5**

Crossnumbers

A

[1]3	6	[2]5		[3]2	5	0	[4]6
6		0	[5]8	0			2
	[6]5	4	[7]1	6		[8]8	3
[9]1	8		9		[10]4	1	
2		[11]2	2	9		0	[12]8
5		1		[13]2	[14]6		7
[15]1	[16]1	0	1		[17]4	0	0
	8		[18]1	2	8		3

B

[1]3	2	[2]5		[3]4	4	4	[4]4
2		0	[5]4	9			5
	[6]3	0	[7]5	5		[8]2	1
[9]9	5		8		[10]6	0	
9		[11]1	8	0		7	[12]3
9		0		[13]6	[14]3		3
[15]9	[16]9	0	0		[17]6	2	0
	9		[18]8	5	0		0

C

[1]1	2	[2]1		[3]1	4	1	[4]5
1		0	[5]5	5			6
	[6]2	8	[7]8	3		[8]8	0
[9]1	1		5		[10]3	2	
0		[11]1	6	7		7	[12]1
6		8		[13]1	[14]5		5
[15]6	[16]9	0	0		[17]1	2	1
	6		[18]5	0	0		2

Page 307 **A long time ago! 5**

1. Cannot be done

Page 308 **Mental Arithmetic Test 1**

1. £35	**2.** 122	**3.** £22	**4.** $\frac{7}{100}$	**5.** 12
6. 64	**7.** $\frac{1}{2}$	**8.** equilateral	**9.** 4.7	**10.** 1, 2, 3, 6
11. 1h 35 min	**12.** 3.5 cm	**13.** 2400	**14.** 17 or 19	**15.** 10
16. n^2	**17.** £60	**18.** 24	**19.** obtuse	**20.** 9

Page 308 **Test 2**

1. 6	**2.** 199	**3.** 380	**4.** 220	**5.** 13%
6. 1999	**7.** 32	**8.** $\frac{1}{5}$	**9.** £3.51	**10.** Hannah by 10 mins
11. 20	**12.** 60	**13.** 75°	**14.** 3	**15.** 8
16. $\frac{7}{12}$	**17.** 2 (or 4 for a square)	**18.** 185	**19.** 201	**20.** 3600

Unit 6

Page 310 **Exercise 1M**

1. (a) 16   (b) 7   (c) 8   (d) 5   (e) 32   (f) 7

2. (a) 5   (b) 8   (c) 2   (d) 10   (e) 4   (f) 9

3. 6   **4.** (a) 40   (b) 36   (c) 35   (d) 30   (e) 66

   (f) 81   **5.** (a) 6   (b) 3   (c) $7\frac{1}{2}$ (d) 7   (e) 12

   (f) 8   **6.** 9   **7.** (a) 5   (b) 6   (c) 30   (d) 4

   (e) 25   (f) 100

Page 311 **Exercise 1E**

1. (a) $\frac{2}{7}$ (b) $\frac{3}{4}$ **2.** (a) $\frac{4}{5}$ (b) $\frac{4}{7}$ (c) $\frac{2}{3}$ (d) $\frac{3}{7}$

   (e) $\frac{2}{13}$ (f) $\frac{3}{5}$ **3.** (a) $\frac{1}{6}$ (b) $\frac{3}{8}$ (c) $\frac{1}{2}$ (d) $\frac{7}{10}$

   (e) $\frac{7}{12}$ (f) $\frac{7}{8}$ **4.** 15   **5.** $n = 5$, length = 17 cm, width = 5 cm

6. (a) $\frac{3}{5}$ (b) 2   (c) 7   (d) $\frac{7}{9}$ (e) 10   (f) $\frac{5}{2} = 2\frac{1}{2}$

   (g) $\frac{9}{2} = 4\frac{1}{2}$ (h) $\frac{16}{5} = 3\frac{1}{5}$ (i) $\frac{11}{6} = 1\frac{5}{6}$

Page 313 **Exercise 1M**

1. (b) 3 times   **2.** 4 times   **3.** (c) 2 times, add 1   **4.** (c) 4 times, add 1

5. (b) 'is 4 more than the number of pink squares'.   **6.** $s = 3n$; $s = 4n$; $s = 2n + 1$; $s = 4n + 1$

Page 315 **Exercise 2M**

1. (a) 6   (b) 12   (c) 60   **2.** (a) 7   (b) 15

   (c) 205   **3.** (a) 7, 14, 21, 28   (b) 4, 5, 6, 7   (c) 4, 7, 10, 13   (d) 24, 23, 22, 21

   (e) 11, 15, 19, 23   **4.** (a) 10n   (b) 3n   (c) 4n + 1   (d) 50n   (e) n^2

   (f) 2n + 6   (g) 3n + 8   (h) 12n

5. (a) M5 = 20, M6 = 24, N5 = 22, N6 = 26   (b) M15 = 60, N20 = 82

6. 3:(6, 6); 5:(10, 10); 40:(80, 80); 45:(90, 90)   **7.** (a) (10, 3)   (b) (100, 3)   (c) (101, 1)

   (d) (201, 1)   **8.** (a) (16, 4)   (b) (80, 4)   (c) (8000, 4)

Page 317 **Investigation – count the crossovers**

Part D: 20 lines have 190 crossovers $\left(\dfrac{20 \times 19}{2}\right)$

Page 318   **Check Yourself on Sections 6.1 and 6.2**

1. (a) 9   (b) 56   (c) 8   (d) $\frac{5}{6}$ (e) 2   (f) $\frac{3}{4}$

2. (c) 2 times, add 6   (d) 43

Page 319   **Exercise 1M**

1. (a) 400 cm   (b) 260 cm   (c) 3 cm   (d) 90 cm   **2.** (a) 2 km
    (b) 4.6 km   (c) 0.75 m   (d) 300 km   **3.** (a) 8000 g   (b) 1800 g
    (c) 200 g   (d) 35 g   **4.** (a) 7000 kg   (b) 20 000 kg   (c) 6.5 kg
    (d) 0.4 kg   **5.** 38 000 g   **6.** 500 cm   **7.** 9000 g   **8.** 0.6 kg
9. 3500 m   **10.** 60 mm   **11.** 4 cm   **12.** 0.7 m   **13.** 4000 ml
14. 2400 g   **15.** 6000 kg   **16.** 20 cm   **17.** 0.5 kg   **18.** 7000 ml
19. 62 000 ml   **20.** 8400 g   **21.** 2.5 litres   **22.** 4.6 cm   **23.** 630 cm
24. 850 g   **25.** 0.3 kg   **26.** (a) 0.95 kg   (b) 25 000 kg   (c) 0.02 kg
27. (a) 0.4 m   (b) 900 m   (c) 0.06 m

Page 320   **Exercise 1E**

1. 36 litres   **2.** 8.8 pounds   **3.** 150 cm   **4.** 45 litres   **5.** 4 feet
6. 4 gallons   **7.** 10 miles   **8.** 48 km   **9.** 27 litres   **10.** 40 km
11. 20 kg   **12.** 50 miles   **13.** 10 feet   **14.** 4 miles   **15.** No
16. Luke   **17.** 150 miles   **18.** Yes   **19.** 800 km   **20.** 22.5 miles

Page 321   **Exercise 2M**

1. (a) 40, 60   (b) 20   **2.** (a) 8, 10.5   (b) 2.5
3. (a) 3.2, 3.9   (b) 0.7   **4.** (a) 55, 80   (b) 25
5. (a) 0.5, 3   (b) 2.5   **6.** (a) 300, 450   (b) 150
7. (a) 4.7, 6.5   (b) 1.8   **8.** (a) 3.5, 5.3   (b) 1.8
9. (a) 400, 900   (b) 500   **10.** (a) 1.5, 3   (b) 1.5
11. (a) 3.8, 4.6   (b) 0.8   **12.** (a) 5.4, 6.7   (b) 1.3
13. (a) 1.3, 3.2   (b) 0.9   **14.** (a) 50, 190   (b) 140
15. (a) 3.5   (b) 125   (c) 0.5   (d) 12.5
16. (a) 2kg   (b) 10 litres   (c) 4 pounds

Page 323   **Exercise 2E**

1. (a) 345 cm   (b) 800 g   (c) 5326 m   (d) 4.8 cm   (e) 1.565 kg   (f) 55 mm
2. (a) 5700 ml   (b) 0.91 m   (c) 3700 kg   (d) 8900 g   (e) 614 g   (f) 8 cm
3. (a) 10 000 cm^2 (b) 3400 cm^2 (c) 800 cm^2 **4.** (a) 440 cm   (b) 120 cm   (c) 780 cm
5. 4.4 cm^2

Page 324   **Check Yourself on Section 6.3**

1. (a) 7000 m   (b) 40 cm   (c) 7.5 litres   (d) 4800 g
2. (a) 6.6 pounds   (b) 36 litres   (c) 64 km   (d) 5 cm

3. (a) 2.5   (b) 0.25   (c) 1.6

4. (a) 6140 g   (b) P by 300 cm^2 (or 0.03 m^2)

Page 325   **Exercise 1M**

1. (a) false   (b) true   (c) true   (d) true   (e) true   (f) false

3. (d), (f)   **4.** (a) 45°   (b) 49°   (c) 65°   (d) 95°

5. (a) $m = 50°$ (b) $n = 77°$ (c) $v = 60°, w = 120°$ (d) $x = 46°, y = 62°$

6. (a) 131°   (b) 22°

Page 326   **Exercise 1E**

1. $a = 120°$ **2.** $b = 120°$ **3.** $c = 47°$ **4.** $d = 73°$

5. $e = 80°, f = 80°, g = 20°$ **6.** $h = 75°, j = 30°$ **7.** $k = 60°, l = 60°$

8. $m = 63°, n = 54°$ **9.** No   **10.** Yes   **11.** 98°   **12.** 30°

Page 328   **Exercise 2M**

1. 57°   **2.** 29°   **3.** 84°   **4.** 103°   **5.** 40°

6. 40°   **7.** 49°   **8.** 98°

Page 333   **Exercise 1M**

1. A–cube, B–cuboid, C–triangular prism, D–hexagonal prism, H–cylinder

2. E–triangular based pyramid (tetrahedron), F–square based pyramid, G–cone, I–sphere, J–hemisphere

3. (a)   (b) $F + V - 2 = E$

	faces	edges	vertices
A	6	12	8
B	6	12	8
C	5	9	6
D	8	18	12
E	4	6	4
F	5	8	5

Page 333   **Exercise 1E**

1. cuboids: 6 faces, 12 edges, 8 vertices   **2.** triangular prisms: 5 faces, 9 edges, 6 vertices

3. remaining shape: 7 faces, 15 edges, 10 vertices
    piece cut off: 4 faces, 6 edges, 4 vertices

4. various answers   **5.** various answers   **7.** Eight shapes can be made.

Page 335   **Exercise 2M**

1. (c) does not make a cube; (a), (b), (d), (e) do make cubes

2. (a) C   (b) F   (d) D   (e) C

Page 337   **Check Yourself on Sections 6.4 and 6.5**

1. (a) 79°   (b) 82°   (c) 22°   **2.** 83°/84°

3. 3.7 cm   **4.** (a) cone   (b) triangular prism   (c) cylinder

5. (a) 5 faces, 8 edges, 5 vertices   (b) 7 faces, 15 edges, 10 vertices

6. (a) and (c)

Page 339   **Mixed Review   Part one**

1. 31   **2.** 5.75 kg   **3.** cube   **4.** 84   **5.** (a) litres
   (b) grams   (c) metres   (d) kilometres   (e) millilitres   (f) centimetres

6. (a) 21   (b) 4   (c) 4   (d) 7   (e) 36
   (f) 6   **7.** 11.7 cm   **8.** sphere   **9.** (a) BC   (b) JK
   (c) H   **10.** 45   **11.** (a) 57°   (b) 59°   **13.** 35 miles

14. (a) true   (b) false   (c) false   (d) true   (e) true
   (f) false   **15.** 240 g

Page 340   **Part two**

1. (a) 3.65 m   (b) 0.85 kg   (c) 49 cm   (d) 4200 g   (e) 0.38 m
   (f) 4.6 cm   **2.** square-based pyramid   **3.** 55°   **4.** (c) 27
   (d) diagram number × 5 + 2   **6.** (a) 28   (b) 4 cm   **7.** 64 g

8. (a) $\frac{2}{3}$ (b) $\frac{6}{7}$ (c) $\frac{7}{5} = 1\frac{2}{5}$ **9.** a = 6, b = 4, c = 5, d = 6, e = 4, f = 5

10. (a) 65536   (b) 4194304   **11.** 90°   **12.** prisms   **13.** 90 km

14. £637   **15.** (a) WE NEED MORE SUMS   (b) HAVE A NICE DAY
   (c) SPURS ARE RUBBISH   (d) PLEASE SET MORE WORK